Studies in

THE BIBLE AND SCIENCE

Studies in

THE BIBLE AND SCIENCE

or

Christ and Creation

by

Henry M. Morris

PRESBYTERIAN AND REFORMED PUBLISHING CO.

Philadelphia, Pennsylvania

Library of Congress Catalog Card Number: 66-16684

First printing, April 1966
Second printing, June 1967
Third printing, September 1968

Printed in the United States of America

FOREWORD

Twenty-five hundred years ago, Daniel the Prophet received a remarkable foreview of future history from an angel sent from God. This marvelous prophecy, found in Chapters 10, 11, and 12 of the book of Daniel, is climaxed by the succinct statement:

> But thou, O Daniel, shut up the words, and seal the book, even to the time of the end: many shall run to and fro, and knowledge shall be increased (Daniel 12:4).

If the time of the end is thus to be characterized by "many" speeding back and forth, traveling about from one destination to another, and by a rapid proliferation of all kinds of knowledge, then we may well be entering the latter days! In less than a century, mankind has progressed from the horse-drawn vehicles which had served his travel needs for all previous millennia to. steam engines and automobiles and airplanes and now to spacecraft which can circumnavigate the earth itself in a hundred minutes! Men in every business and profession are frequently traveling to and fro, in jet planes or on super-highways, for one appointment after another. It is commonplace now to travel across the continent by auto in days, or by plane in hours, but only a few decades ago such a trip consumed many months and entailed often insuperable hardships.

"And knowledge shall be increased." The population explosion of these last times is trivial in comparision with the explosion of knowledge. No longer is a college education a luxury to be obtained by only a privileged few. The nation's colleges and universities are expanding at fantastic rates, but not rapidly enough to keep up with the numbers seeking admission. The growth of knowledge in any one of a thousand different disciplines of study is now far beyond the capabilities of even the expert practitioners of the discipline to keep up with. If one tried to read all the publications coming out even in his own specialty, he would never have time for anything else, and still could not read as fast as the words keep coming! This strange situation is pointed up also by the fact that research divisions of many industries commonly estimate it is cheaper to repeat a research program than to try to find out if it has already been done. A recent review of the problems posed by the "information explosion" says:

> A thorough literature search is so expensive, one steel company estimated it would be cheaper to spend up to $100,000 and risk duplication.[1]

---

[1]Bruce H. Frisch: "The Big Information Mess," *Science Digest*, Vol. 58, September 1965, p. 24.

It has been estimated that, of all the scientists who have ever lived since time began, more than 90% are living today! This proliferation of knowledge and scientists has resulted in a proliferation and continuous subdividing of scientific specialties, each with its own particular scientific journals. The number of *different* scientific periodicals now being published in the world has been estimated as perhaps 100,000! No library, even the Library of Congress, can any longer hope to provide space for the floods of technical literature pouring off the presses.

Under such circumstances, it is obviously ridiculous for any scientist to be classed as an "authority" in any subject broader than the particular problems on which he himself is conducting research. A Ph.D. degree in Geology, for example, is evidence only that the holder has a fair reading acquaintance with geological terminology and the broader outlines of the scope of earth science, but it is quite impossible for him actually to have special, first-hand knowledge of any of the details of more than a highly restricted area of study. He may be a paleontologist, a hydrogeologist, a sedimentologist, a geophysicist, a petrologist, a hydrologist, a geochemist, a volcanologist, or any one of a dozen more major specialties. If he is, say, a paleontologist, he will specialize in some sub-discipline such as perhaps micropaleontology, and will attempt to become an "authority" in, let us say, the "Foraminifera of the Middle Eocene Epoch in Western Europe," or some such study. By dint of much field and library research, he might really become an authority on this subject, but this would require so much time and effort that he could hardly be expected to become an authority on anything else, or at least on not more than a few other special topics of this sort.

In a little more personal vein, the writer's field is that of civil engineering, and he has had a certain amount of training and experience in the field as a whole. However, civil engineering is a very broad field embracing many specialties (structural design, soil mechanics, traffic engineering, surveying, sanitary engineering, highway design, construction management, and others). The writer's field of special training and experience is that of hydraulic engineering and hydrology. But this also is a very broad division of civil engineering, involving a great many specialties and many different journals. Even with graduate degrees in this field, and even as the author of a fairly widely-used textbook[2] in applied hydraulics, he still cannot claim to have really intensive knowledge in many of the areas of active hydraulic and hydrolo-

---

[2]*"Applied Hydraulics in Engineering"* (New York, Ronald Press, 1963, 455 pp.)

gic study. The general subject of "turbulent flow over rough boundaries" is the topic which the writer has studied most thoroughly and in which perhaps he has made some contribution, but even on this rather specialized subject, the amount of literature being published is more than he can keep up with.

The point of all this is to emphasize that no man living can claim to be an "authority" in science in general or even in any one science. And above all, no man can possibly presume to make such a statement as: "Science contradicts the Bible," or "The world-view necessitated by modern science disproves the Biblical cosmology." The fact that such statements are made, and in fact quite frequently made, is a sad testimonial to the immodesty and presumption of many scientists, who are merely fallible and sinful human beings like all other men.

The Bible claims to be the very Word of God, and it has been accepted as such by multitudes of intelligent people down through the centuries. This is more true today than ever in the past, with at least many hundreds of highly qualified scientists around the world known quite definitely to believe in the full verbal inspiration and infallibility of the Holy Scriptures. Any possible "authority" which these men may have in their own fields of science of course does not of itself verify the truth of the Bible (which stands quite on its own, without the need of any human confirmation), but the fact does at least belie the frequent claim that no scientist believes the Bible.

As the Word of God, the Bible speaks authoritatively on every subject with which it deals, not only those subjects which are mainly moral and religious, but also those associated with the physical phenomena of the world in which we live. Since there are hundreds of Biblical passages dealing with such phenomena, there are many points of contact between Scripture and science. A study of the relation between science and the Bible cannot help, therefore, being practical and interesting to all who are interested in science.

The writer can testify that such has proved abundantly true in his own experience. There are numerous passages in Scripture dealing with the phenomena of hydrology, for example, and all will be found fully in accord with what is known from actual studies in this field of science. It has been a richly stimulating experience to try to make detailed studies of the numerous Biblical references to scientific facts in their relation to the character of those facts as reported by practitioners in the respective fields of science with which they deal.

Not only has the writer found this true in his own experience, but he has observed it to be true in the experience of many others. He has been publishing books in this field for many years,[3] and a total of over 120,000 copies of these books have been printed to date. The correspondence resulting from these, as well as the personal contacts resulting from speaking on these subjects in over 20 different states has shown beyond doubt that there are great numbers of intelligent people, including hundreds of scientists, who find such studies very rewarding, and who are fully convinced that the Bible is completely reliable and very incisive in all its references to the facts and theories of modern science.

Along with the books, the writer has written a number of shorter articles and papers, which have been published in various places. Since there are frequent requests for these, it has seemed advisable to try to collect these all under one cover, and this is the purpose of the present book.

Since these were originally published separately, there is necessarily a lack of continuity from one chapter to the next. Also there is bound to be some overlap of subject matter, though not a great deal. All things considered, it seemed that the best way of organizing the material would be chronological, simply arranging the chapters in the order of their respective times of publication. This would at least serve to show the general development of interest and study in different topics with the passage of time, extending over nearly the past 20 years.

A few changes have been made in each of most of the original articles, in order to make them more pertinent to the present context. Despite the lack of continuity, and some duplication, it is hoped that this collection will prove helpful. Many different topics have been treated, but all are presented within the interpretive framework of a firm conviction that the Holy Scriptures are fully inspired, authoritative, and perspicuous, and that all the data and theories of modern science must be brought within this framework for their full and proper understanding.

The final chapter, "Christ in Creation," has not previously been published elsewhere. It has been written in order to emphasize that, in all of our studies of the wonderful universe that God

---

[3]For the record, and for possible reference, these books are as follows:
That You Might Believe (Chicago, Good Books, Inc., 1946), 156 pp.
The Bible and Modern Science (Chicago, Moody Press, 1951) 151 pp.
The Bible and Modern Science (Paperback, Chicago, Moody Press, 1957), 128 pp.
The Genesis Flood (with John C. Whitcomb, Jr.,) Philadelphia, Presbyterian and Reformed Publishing Co., 1961) 518 pp.
Biblical Catastrophism and Geology (Paper, Presbyterian and Reformed, 1963), 15 pp.
The Twilight of Evolution (Baker, Grand Rapids, 1964), 103 pp.

has established and of the even more wonderful Scriptures which He has given, the Lord Jesus Christ is Himself the focus and goal of it all. He is both the Creator and the Upholder of all things, and the unifying theme of all the Scriptures. He is Saviour and Lord.

> But of Him are ye in Christ Jesus, who of God is made unto us wisdom, and righteousness, and sanctification, and redemption (I Corinthians 1:30).
> For of Him, and through Him, and to Him, are all things: to whom be glory for ever. Amen (Romans 11:36).

Acknowledgments

Several of the articles in this volume have been reviewed prior to their original publication by Dr. John Whitcomb, Professor of Old Testament at Grace Seminary in Winona Lake, Indiana. Dr. Whitcomb is co-author of Chapter V, "The Genesis Flood — Its Nature and Significance." A large number of individual pastors and laymen have indirectly contributed through discussion and fellowship, and appreciation is expressed to all of these.

Special thanks are due to Dr. Walter E. Lammerts, Chairman of the Creation Research Society, who has reviewed the revised manuscript in its entirety.

In addition, the writer desires to recognize and thank specifically those organizations and publications that have allowed the reprinting of these articles in this form. These include the following:

HIS MAGAZINE. Monthly periodical of the Inter-Varsity Christian Fellowship, 1519 N. Astor Street, Chicago, Illinois. The I.V.C.F. is an inter-denominational student organization with chapters on hundreds of college campuses in this country.

GOOD NEWS PUBLISHING CO., Westchester, Illinois. Publishers of gospel tracts and booklets, and condensed Christian books.

CHRISTIAN LIFE MAGAZINE, Gunderson Dr. at Schmale Rd., Wheaton, Ill. An inter-denominational monthly for general reading.

BIBLIOTHECA SACRA. The quarterly theological journal of Dallas Theological Seminary, 3909 Swiss Avenue, Dallas, Texas. In the writer's opinion, this is the finest Bible study publication of an inter-denominational nature being produced in this country. It is the oldest such publication in terms of years of continuous publication, and the Dallas Seminary is the largest non-denominational, conservative seminary.

TORCH AND TRUMPET., Breton Village, Grand Rapids, Michigan. The monthly publication of the Reformed Fellowship, Inc., sponsored by a group of ministers and laymen in the Christian Reformed

Church, along with others committed to traditional reformed theology.

COLLEGIATE CHALLENGE. An evangelistic magazine published four times annually and directed toward the end of winning college students for Christ. Published by the Campus Crusade for Christ, Arrowhead Springs, San Bernardino, California. The Campus Crusade is actively promoting intensive and successful evangelistic programs on many campuses.

GRACE JOURNAL. The quarterly theological journal of the Grace Theological Seminary in Winona Lake, Indiana. The journal and seminary are part of the Grace Brethren denomination.

CREATION RESEARCH SOCIETY QUARTERLY. Published by the Creation Research Society, 4090 Geddes Road, Ann Arbor, Michigan. The Creation Research Society is an organization of approximately 300 scientists committed to research in the problem areas related to science and the Bible. These scientists have at least the equivalent of an M.S. degree and, in addition, are Biblical Christians, believing in the verbal inspiration of Scripture, the deity and blood atonement of the Lord Jesus Christ, the literal truth of the Genesis Creation record and the universality of the Deluge.

GOOD NEWS BROADCASTER. An outstanding monthly family magazine published by the Back-To-The-Bible Broadcast, Lincoln, Nebraska.

Most of the articles in this compendium were compiled and issued in syllabus form in 1963 by the Grace Seminary, as edited by Dr. John Whitcomb. When that printing was exhausted, it was decided then to organize them into this more complete and permanent form. Re-typing of the manuscripts has been the contribution of the writer's mother.

The writer desires also to express appreciation to the publisher, Mr. Charles Hays Craig, not only for a very pleasant association in connection with the publication of this and other books, but also for his willingness to allow the writer full freedom in the expression of his own theological convictions. As a Baptist and moderate dispensationalist, the writer has occasionally written items with which a thorough-going Reformed theologian such as Mr. Craig might wish to take issue. If such items appear in these pages, the writer of course wishes to take full responsibility. Both author and publisher, of course, fully concur in the great truths of the everlasting Gospel of our Lord Jesus Christ, and the complete integrity and authority of every portion of Holy Scripture, the defense and proclamation of which is the purpose of this book.

CONTENTS

11

I

REASON AND THE CHRISTIAN HOPE[1]

Can We Know That Christianity Is True?

The Origin of the Universe

It is certain that the universe as we know it must have had a definite beginning. The older philosophies of the eternity of matter have been set aside by modern physics and astronomy. Jeans compares the universe to a clock that is running down. The relentless Second Law of Thermodynamics states that every energy change or transfer must be in a downward direction, as far as the usability of the energy is concerned. Every mechanical device of man's invention delivers less energy than it receives, the remainder being dissipated in friction in unrecoverable heat energy. The same principle applies throughout all nature. Suns and stars continually send out tremendous quantities of energy, most of which is lost in space.

Obviously, this cannot go on forever. Either the universe must eventually die a "heat death" or some unknown principle or person must sometime, somehow intervene to renew it. Equally obviously, this cannot have been going on forever in the past. There must, beyond any question or cavil, have been a beginning, when the universe was much more highly charged with energy in a high degree of availability than it is now.

As to who or what began it, we can conceive of only two alternatives. There is the possibility that some impersonal principle (call it chance or what you will), something intrinsic in the natural order of things, about whose origin we can know nothing, somehow shaped things into their initial form, and then set them to following out a deterministic process of development, or rather degeneration. Or, there is the possibility that all things were created in the beginning by a Person, also about whose origin we know nothing. It comes to this: The universe was begun either by a Person, or by something without personality.

But if the law of cause and effect means anything, the universe could only have been brought into existence by a *cause* adequate

[1]This article was originally published in booklet form by the Tract Club of America, Chicago, Illinois, in 1947. It was also reprinted in part in *Prophecy Monthly*, Vol. 20, April 1948, pp. 9-11.

to account for every thing, every concept, every character exhibited by the universe. It is axiomatic, at least as far as anything now going on in the universe is concerned, that the effect cannot be greater than the cause. A cause must have at least all the characters of the effect it produces. How, then, can it be possible, even by a nearly interminable process of evolution to produce intelligence, to produce feeling, emotion, will — in short, to produce personality (which is beyond doubt an effect observable in the universe and in our own self-consciousness), if the cause is not itself possessed of personality?

Some philosophers have attempted to deny the validity of the reasoning processes when applied to such matters as the above; others have sought to question the applicability of the law of cause and effect when applied to questions of origins. Such speculations, however, are completely divorced from the world of reality that we know, a world in which cause and effect do operate, and in which logical reasoning based on correct premises leads to correct conclusions.

Therefore, the only reasonable conclusion, if causality means anything, is that the universe and everything in it was created by a great personality — by God. This does not necessarily prove that the great First Cause is the God revealed in Scripture, but it does prove (to the extent that science and human reasoning are able to *prove anything!*) that He must be a Personal God, and not an impersonal Force of some kind.

One further conclusion comes easily. There is something in our own finite personalities that we call a conscience or a moral urge. Whatever it is, each individual, however benighted, recognizes something in him that tells him that he ought to do the thing that is right morally and ought to shun the wrong — even though individual standards as to what constitutes right and wrong seem to vary somewhat with time and place. As far as personalities in the universe are concerned, at least, it is a moral universe. Therefore, the Creator is a moral being, who has placed in His creatures a moral consciousness. One more inference, perhaps not rigidly necessary but certainly logical, is that this consciousness of moral values implies a moral responsibility to the Giver of that consciousness.

Thus, we have found it reasonable to believe in a Personal God, who has created and who sustains the universe by the Word of His Power. As the highest of His creatures, man also has personality. He has intelligence to comprehend and study an intelligent universe, he possesses a moral sense which he intuitively realizes implies a moral responsibility to God, he has a will which enables him and impels him to make moral choices, and he has emotional capabilities for love, for hate, for joy, sorrow, anger, peace — which emotions must inevitably be related to his moral nature and ultimately to his relation with God.

Man's Purpose and Destiny

It is the belief of the best among men that the highest emotion, the noblest motivation, is that of love. If love prevailed among men and nations, there would be no war, no crime, no suffering, no want. God has placed the capacity to love and the desire for love at the very center of man's personality. By causal reasoning, if nothing more, we can be certain that love is likewise at the very heart of the personality of God. We may find it difficult to reconcile the evil and suffering in the world with this fact of God's love, but surely the presence of love and goodness and beauty in the world and the instinctive recognition of all men that these things are better and more to be desired than evil and hatred should satisfy the minds and hearts of right-thinking men that God is a God of love, as well as a God of holiness.

Because of these facts, we must believe that the creation of man is intimately connected with God's nature of love. It is clearly conceivable that God has created man in His own spiritual likeness, in order that He might have someone on whom to lavish the love flowing from His own nature, and someone that would freely and voluntarily reciprocate that love.

Man's chief purpose then, it is quite reasonable to believe, is to love and to be loved by God. This is a logical, and certainly the most ennobling, explanation of the existence of love in the universe and in individuals.

God's love, however, cannot be exercised at the cost of His holiness, His righteousness, His justice. There can be no possibility of an infinitely holy Creator allowing wrong to go overlooked or unpunished. But the possibility of wrong entering the universe and thriving for a time cannot be doubted. Beyond dispute, there is, experimentally, much of evil and suffering in the world. Therefore, even though we must conceive of God as perfectly holy in all His actions and plans, we must also concede that somehow in the infinitude of His creation, there exists the possibility of unholiness — of sin.

Indeed, it is difficult even to think of good, except in opposition to bad, of truth except as against falsehood, of holiness except as contrasted with sinfulness. The good qualities can mean nothing unless freely chosen and exhibited in preference to the bad. A properly designed machine could deserve no credit and would elicit no love for accurately and dependably doing what was expected of it; it has no choice in the matter.

Now, if man's chief end is to love God — to satisfy the longing of the God of love for the love of creatures of His own image — there must obviously be real moral freedom on the part of man to exercise that love; otherwise, he would be a mere piece of machinery, and God would derive no satisfaction from an involuntary love — indeed such a love is inconceivable and involves a contradiction in terms.

But, patently, moral freedom involves the possibility of a thoroughly wrong moral choice, of hate or indifference instead of love, of doubt instead of faith, of a desire for independence from God rather than a loving trust in Him. That such a wrong choice has been made by mankind, and by individual men, cannot be doubted.

Here is the explanation, very clearly, for our own lack of knowledge of the person of God, our lack of the fellowship with Him for which we were created. We have chosen wrongly, and His holiness cannot permit fellowship with sinners. We have, of our own volition, rejected His proferred love and righteousness, for independence and sin, and have therefore hindered Him from exercising His love toward us as He otherwise would. It is our own sins that have separated us from our God, and there is no way of our undoing them, or starting over. We cannot call back all the lies, the cursing, the bitterness that have escaped our lips, nor can we unthink all the evil thoughts or undo the evil deeds of which we have been guilty, and that have continued to pain the heart of God and to separate us yet further from Him. We are by all rights completely and eternally lost from God's presence and His plan for us.

God's Plan of Redemption

But it does not seem reasonable that God would leave His creatures in this condition without doing something else, making possible a restoration. He, being omniscient, must have foreseen all that has taken place, before the beginning of the creation. He created man to love and to be loved and it is inconceivable that God could fail in His purpose. Accordingly, He must have planned from the foundation of the world to work out a redemption for lost mankind. But it is almost impossible to conceive of a method that would do everything necessary and still be consistent with God's character. This plan must be one that would reveal God's holiness to men and that would make them desire holiness and hate sin; it must be something that would adequately and completely remove all the accumulated effects of sin from the characters of men; above all, it must be something that would change the desires and affections of men in such a way that they would no longer be in a condition of rejection of God's will and His love, but would have their love and gratitude drawn out to Him as His love is revealed to them.

None of the ordinary philosophies or religions of men have discovered any such method. It is something that seems to be beyond human wisdom; it is past finding out. We *can* think of *one* way, however; but we could never have thought of it had not God revealed it to us. But having once seen it and believed it, we can see in it the infinite wisdom of God!

God, though infinite, might take upon Himself the form of man, might be made part and parcel of mankind. By a thoroughly human life, He might exhibit in Himself, and in a way that could be understood by men, His own holiness and His love. As the staggering burden of the sins of mankind, of which He then would be a part, would press upon Him, more and more coming into conflict with His nature, He might then allow Himself to bear the weight of all the sins and resultant suffering of all men, ultimately to experience and endure the inconceivable awfulness of hell — to endure what men who have rejected the love and fellowship of God deserve to suffer, the complete absence of that love and fellowship, the presence of nothing but sin, completely forsaken of God.

As yet, we do not realize what it will mean to be completely and eternally cut off from all the evidences and the effects of the presence and love and care of our Creator, but such complete separation is the logical result of our rejection of His love and must eventually be the fruitage of what we have sown. But, if God Himself were to undergo, in substitution, all this suffering for us, may we not be free? — may we not then be restored to our lost estate?

This possibility becomes more evident when it is remembered that God created us for the purpose of loving Him and knowing His love. There is nothing that could so make a man love God — a man who has sinned and is lost from God and can do nothing about his sinfulness — as for that man to know that God Himself has borne and suffered for and carried away his sin. When he rightly views his own lost condition, deserving nothing at all from God, but then seeing God going to such lengths to save him, his whole being must surely be changed. He can and must love God with all his heart and soul; he must be eternally grateful to Him; he must come to love the things God loves and hate the sin that had separated him from God.

But further, it is the infinite God thus suffering for a finite number of finite men. And though his suffering under such circumstances may have been infinite, as far as we can understand, it could not be eternal. He who is the Maker of life, He who *is* Life, could not die forever. When His soul is once made an offering for sin, He must prolong His days; He must be alive forevermore.

It is granted that these thoughts do not explain everything about God's plan of redemption. It is too much, too great, too grand for us to comprehend. But at least we have seen it reasonable to believe that God must have taken this course of divine substitution for sinful man. No other plan could be conceived that could accomplish God's purpose for men, that could be consistent with His own character of holiness and love, and that could satisfy His own heart.

Should we not, then, when His person and plan are revealed to us, by His own revelation and by history, thereupon open our hearts to Him, love Him, and serve Him forever? And as our hearts open to His love, is it not possible that all the beauty of His own holiness and all the power of His eternal life, His resurrection life, may become ours?

The Revelation of His Plan

It is obviously possible, as well as reasonable, that God could reveal His plan of redemption to men. In fact, as we have intimated, it is necessary, since the only course that God could follow is incomprehensible to man unless divinely revealed. Still, God must not force the acceptance of it. He desires real love, voluntary love. Not only His character and His creation are now available to elicit such love, but also His marvelous provision of salvation from the penalty and power of sin. This must be revealed to men, but only in such a way as to *encourage* faith and love, not to force them.

Accordingly, we may be sure that God has revealed this plan to men in some definite way, *but not in such a way as to be beyond doubt*. There must be either the promise of His plan to be worked out, or the record of His plan having been worked out, or both — and they must now be available to all men who *desire* to know God and to be restored to His fellowship.

Thus, we can be satisfied that none of the religious or philosophical systems of the past, now dead, were true revelations of God; had they been, God would not have allowed them to die out. Similarly, we can infer that none of the purely local or national religions are true revelations of God; all men need to know of God's plan, and therefore, the true religion must be missionary.

Besides Christianity, only Buddhism and Mohammedanism meet

even these two qualifications. It is evident that only *one* of these three can be God's true revelation, because each is radically different from the others, especially in the all-important matter of the way of salvation. Buddhism has rather markedly degenerated from the form of its original enunciation, but both originally and now emphasizes good works as the means of salvation. It is mostly silent about God; there is nothing whatever in it to draw out man's love toward his Creator and Redeemer. The Moslem conception of God is somewhat similar to that of Christianity, but the incentive to obey Him is not that of love for Him, but rather fear of hell, and the promise of a very sensual paradise to the faithful follower of Mohammed.

Neither Buddhism nor Islam knows anything of the grace of God, nor of obedient love in response to that grace. Buddhism is a missionary religion, or was, but it was spread mostly by political power and by compromise with and absorption of other existing religions. The Moslem religion was spread mostly by the sword, wielded in the hands of fanatical followers fighting those who would not accept Mohammed as the last and greatest prophet of God. Christianity has spread around the world as a result of neither force nor compromise, but through the transformed lives and the loving testimony of those who have believed that "God was in Christ, reconciling the world unto Himself."

The Testimony of History

Today, great numbers of people, though admittedly a small minority of all mankind, believe that God was born into the world as a man some 1960 years ago as Jesus of Nazareth, that He lived a sinless life, that He died on the cross of Calvary as the divine Substitute and Saviour of all men, that He rose bodily from the grave three days later, and ascended into heaven, there to wait until the time of His return as the Judge of the world.

These beliefs, and the Christian Church built around and upon them, have existed in the same essential form since the time of Christ Himself. This much can be denied by no one who is at all acquainted with the facts. All the evidences of archaeological discovery, textual criticism, the writings of early church fathers and every other pertinent line of objective evidence assure us that the Christians of the first century, many of whom had known the Lord Jesus Himself, thoroughly believed in a thoroughly supernatural Christ, one who had performed mighty miraculous works and who had Himself risen from the dead and in whose atoning death was their hope of salvation and eternal life.

It is also a matter of certain history that these early Christians suffered terrible persecution, often martyrdom, for their beliefs. Surely they had every reason to examine most thoroughly the grounds for their faith, the reason for their hope. Yet in spite of every inducement to recant, their testimony held firm, and "so, mightily grew the Word of God and prevailed."

It is beyond the scope of this article to discuss it, but the antiquity and authenticity of the New Testament writings have been abundantly confirmed. There can be little doubt that, in the Gospels, we have the apostolic writings in essentially their original form. Thus, if they do not reveal Christ as He really was, and the things He actually said and did, only two things are possible. The early Christian leaders were either fools or frauds.

If they, for some reason, were attempting to produce false records, perhaps in order to establish a new religon, there is no getting around the fact that they were deliberate liars. But surely no one who has fairly read the Gospels could charge the writers of such marvelous documents with fraud or forgery. There are overpowering internal evidences against such a notion, but the conclusive thing is this: men do not suffer willingly and gladly, materially and physically, for something they know to be a lie. Many false causes have their martyrs, of course, but always they believe implicitly in their cause. But it is absolutely inconceivable that the early Christian writers and leaders could have conspired in a deliberate fraud and then gone forth to suffer the loss of their possessions and friends, to endure the most severe physical persecution, and finally to prison and death — all for preaching a gospel they knew to be false. No, there are some things that just cannot be.

But admitting they were sincere in what they preached and wrote, could they not have been mistaken? Well, they certainly had every reason to examine this possibility. But they wrote about things they had actually seen and heard out in the open, among crowds of people. They were not epileptic visionaries, recording dreams and mysteries. They saw and handled the body of the risen Saviour. They knew that the body, which had been placed in Joseph's tomb, was no longer there. And, incidentally, if the body of Jesus had been available, the Jews would most certainly have produced it to halt the spreading "heresy" about His resurrection.

Thus, it is nothing less than absurdity — the claim that the early Christians were either deluded or deceivers. There is, then, one and only one conclusion. Christ *did* conquer death. He *was* God manifest in the flesh. The Christian faith is founded on *absolute historic truth!*

The Written Word of God

Thus far, we have carefully refrained from basing any of our arguments upon the teachings of the Bible. Many, of course, don't admit or believe the Bible to be the inspired Word of God and thus appeals based on its authority can have very little weight with them. Consequently, we have first attempted to show that Christianity is thoroughly consistent with and satisfying to all *true* reason, even apart from Scripture.

But this by no means implies that we do not or should not believe in the absolute inerrancy and authority of the Bible. We have seen the reasonableness and necessity of a revelation from God, and that this revelation must be in Christianity. But it is the Bible that contains this revelation — nay, the Bible *is* this revelation.

In support of such a tremendous assertion, it should be stressed that, whether inspired or not, the Bible is an absolutely unique book. It is the world's all-time best seller. More books have been written about it, even more books written against it, than any other book. It is the only book that has been proved to have a real heart interest for absolutely *every* class of people; it has been translated into more languages, it contains the finest literature, it plumbs the greatest depths, it teaches the highest ethics, it has had the greatest influence on civilization, and it has resulted in more transformed lives than any other book ever written since the dawn of history. None of these positions can be successfully disputed, if indeed anyone would attempt to dispute them.

It contains sixty-six separate books, written by some forty different authors over a period of some fifteen hundred years in widely scattered localities and in every walk of life. The authors, save one, were all Jews; its chief characters are Jews, yet its appeal is universal. And, most marvelous, it is essentially one book, developing one grand theme from beginning to end. The central character is the Son of God, Jesus Christ, and the theme is the eternal plan of redemption for lost mankind.

It is not primarily a book of science, yet contains scores of modern scientific truths, and no scientific errors. It records hundreds of marvelously, precisely fulfilled prophecies.

Surely, no one could expect man alone to produce such a book. No other book in all the world or from all the ages is even remotely comparable. Then, is it not significant that its writers assert over and over and over again that what they wrote came from God? Something like four thousand times, in various ways, appears the assertion that these are the words of God Himself.

Is it possible that the writers of this, the greatest book of all the ages, were fools, fanatics or liars? No, they were what they

claimed to be — "moved by the Holy Ghost," and the Bible is
the Word of the Living God!

There is one standard of ethics all through the Word — the
character of God Himself. Sin in every form is ruthlessly condemned, nothing more so than the sin of hypocrisy and that of
lying. Therefore, sinful, lying men could not, would not, have
written it of their own will. Neither could good men, if there
were such, have written it, because the writers claim that God
wrote it and good men would not lie. God alone could have
given the Bible. Therefore, read it, study it, obey it constantly,
if you would know and do the will of God!

Empirical Demonstration

In science or technology, the accuracy of a theory or an hypothesis is necessarily subject to doubt until put to experimental test.
It must be recognized that in Christianity as well the ultimate
demonstration of its truth awaits the return of Christ. In the
meantime, however, it is empirically proved, millions of times over,
that reception of Christ into the heart of an individual, by faith,
transforms that individual into a new creature, old things having
passed away, and all things having become new (II Corinthians
5:17).

It is admitted immediately that not all professing Christians give
any such evidence of a transformed life. Many consider themselves
Christians on the basis of church membership or baptism or sacra-
ments or a more or less Christian ethical standard. The existence
of such pseudo-Christianity no more disproves the reality of true
Christianity than does the imitation diamond disprove the genuine
diamond. Even genuine diamonds may be very rough before
cutting and polishing, and this is true of genuine Christians also.

But the certainty is this: there are great numbers of people,
not yet perfect, but whose lives have been reclaimed from sin,
whose affections have been transferred from the things of earth
and of self to those of God, in whose hearts has been implanted
the love of Christ toward God and toward the brethren. And
these people, with absolute honesty and sincerity, testify that this
change in nature and purpose resulted from their decision to believe in Christ Jesus as the eternal Son of God, and their personal
Saviour.

And so it is that God's eternal purpose for man is being worked
out and fulfilled in the hearts of individuals who see their need
of salvation and long for the lost fellowship with their Creator to
be restored. When they have seen God in Christ taking the guilt
of their sins upon Himself, then has their gratitude and love

flown out toward Him in such a way that He can enter their very souls and restore them to His life and presence. The "love of God constrains them, because they thus judge, that if one died for all, then all were dead, that they which live should not henceforth live unto themselves, but unto Him who died for them and rose again" (II Corinthians 5:14, 15). Joyful obedience and holiness, therefore, spring not from fear of punishment or hope of reward, but from a heart of love and gratitude toward Him who is now not only their Creator, but also their Redeemer.

There is nothing else in all the world like this! None but the Lord Jesus Christ can make holy that which is evil, can bring peace and rest to those who are laboring and burdened, can give joy in sorrow, can bring the assurance of sins having been cleansed and forgiven, can make union with God a reality, can give everlasting life!

We have seen that the Christian hope is reasonable, and uniquely so. Nay, for those who have put their trust in Christ, it is not merely hope, it is certainty. But it is not enough to be mentally satisfied of its truth; one must personally appropriate the Lord Jesus to himself, believing in his heart and soul that Christ, and He alone, can save. "Come unto Me," says Jesus — and — "Him that cometh to Me I will in no wise cast out" (Matthew 11:28, John 6:37).

But to reject God's matchless love-gift, even to neglect it, is to prove that a person does not want to know and love God, that he could never be happy in the presence of God through the eternal ages, that he prefers sin and self to God's righteousness. Therefore, in perfect justice and mercy, God must keep such a one away from His presence forever. This, essentially, is hell — the eternal absence from the presence and the power of God, existence forever in a state of darkness and sin.

In the present economy, God gives each of us the privilege and the necessity of making the choice as to which course we want to follow. His love has given its ultimate expression in order that His holiness may be vindicated. Every individual in the world can be freely and forever saved if he wants to be, if he wants to know God and love and serve Him. "God commendeth His love toward us, in that while we were yet sinners, Christ died for us" (Romans 5:8). "God so loved the world that He gave His only begotten Son, that whosoever believeth in Him should not perish, but have everlasting life" (John 3:16).

But it is in this life only that the decision must be made. In a very real sense, God grants us life here on earth simply in order that our decision may be made and our characters given their eternal inclination. One minute after death, the truth of God's revelation will be instantaneously clear to each soul, but the decision, whatever it is, will have been made previously.

Therefore, may we make a final, personal appeal? God has given us a lifetime in which to choose, but there is no way of knowing how long will be our lifetime. Nothing is assured beyond the very moment you read this line. "Behold, now is the accepted time — now is the day of salvation" (II Corinthians 6:2). "How shall we escape, if we neglect so great salvation?" (Hebrews 2:3).

Drop on your knees now before God and thank Him for His great love, receive the Lord Jesus as your eternal Saviour and King, confess Him before men and seek henceforth to love and live for Him.

"If thou shalt confess with thy mouth Jesus as Lord, and shalt believe in thine heart that God hath raised Him from the dead, thou shalt be saved" (Romans 10:9).

II

THE WONDER OF WATER[1]

Municipal authorities in many cities today are concerned about the dwindling supply of drinking water available. In many areas artesian wells are drying up while water levels in reservoirs continue to drop into danger zones. Industrial, agricultural, recreational, and residential uses of water are growing explosively, and placing an ever-increasing strain on our limited water resources, and the nations are spending vast sums for research on methods for turning salt water into fresh water.

Yet, curiously enough, of all the substances on the surface of the earth there is certainly none so abundant nor so precious as water. Not many people are aware of the fact that nearly three-quarters of the earth's surface is covered by water and that its only possible rival for greatest importance in the material life of mankind is the air we breathe.

In the field of science, a great number of men and women today are engaged in the study of water. A still greater number depend either directly or indirectly upon water for their source of income. Many fields of science and engineering are, therefore, directly dedicated to the study of water. There are hydraulic engineers, irrigation engineers, flood control engineers, hydrodynamicists, hydrographers, oceanographers, hydrochemists, meteorologists, geomorphologists, sanitary engineers, — an almost unending list of specialists studying the sources, uses and effects of water.

It would seem that for such a common substance, and with so much of time and talent being devoted to its study, just about everything that can be known must have been determined already about water. But this is not so. In fact, very little is definitely known about the fundamental laws governing all the multitudinous manifestations of water movement and use.

Despite all this, men seldom consider the miracle of water as the wonder that it is — one of the most marvelous provisions which God has made for the life and comfort of mankind.

It is remarkable that not one of the great number of Biblical references to water is out of accord with the findings of modern science. On the contrary, there are many references which seem to reveal a modern perspective, so modern in fact that it would seem to be inexplicable apart from divine revelation.

---

[1]Originally in *Christian Life*, Vol. 11, August 1949, pp. 19, 20, 44, 48.

The science which, probably more aptly than any other, can be styled the science of water is hydrology, especially when it includes that branch of meteorology dealing with atmospheric moisture. The fundamental law or fact of modern hydrology and meteorology is what is known as the "hydrologic cycle." This cycle is the movement of water after it is precipitated as rain, etc., into the ground and surface waters of the earth, eventually to drain back to the ocean from which it had originally been lifted by evaporation and moved inland by the winds.

It is remarkable that water can be lifted, against the force of gravity, hundreds and thousands of feet into the air and there suspended until it has been moved inland where it is needed. Because there is no agency on the earth sufficiently powerful or ingenious, God has equipped the sun, ninety-three million miles away, to do it.

Liquid water becomes water vapor, at a rate and to an extent dependent upon the temperature, degree of saturation of the adjacent air, etc., and is carried upward by turbulence and diffusion in the gaseous atmosphere. Since gases, including water vapor, expand with increasing temperature, warmer air near the surface tends to rise. On a large scale, the great warm air masses near the equator tend to rise and flow poleward, where the cold air masses, being denser, have settled nearer the ground. Thus, there tends to be a continual movement of warm, equatorial, moisture-laden air toward the poles, and beneath this a movement of cold, dry air toward the equator.

But that is not all. Obviously, it would not be sufficient for God to have provided for the evaporation of the waters from the ocean, only to leave them suspended directly above their former bed.

We have mentioned the great air movement from the equator to the poles and back again. The winds of the world cannot be described so simply as this; they are also influenced by the earth's rotation, the topography, and many other things. However, the major air motions of the world are always of the same kind and follow the same circuits, fulfilling, among other things, the essential purpose of bringing the life-giving waters, cleansed of their salts and impurities, back to the land. It is significant that God, as recorded in Jeremiah 10:13, reminds us that "He bringeth forth the wind out of his treasures." Consider also the statement in the first chapter of Ecclesiastes, verse 6: "The wind goeth toward the south and turneth about unto the north; it whirleth about continually, and the wind returneth again according to his circuits." This is a striking example of modern knowledge, revealed in God's Word nearly 3000 years ago.

An even more interesting Biblical reference concerns the construction of clouds.

Ordinary water vapor, being gaseous, is transparent and is almost always present, to some extent, in the atmosphere. However, God has made very wonderful provision for its being restored to the earth. After it has been moved inland, it may recondense into liquid water in the form of clouds, dew, fog, etc.

For some reason, the particles of water vapor need to have some solid particle of dust or other foreign matter about which to "congeal" into particles of liquid water. The reference in Proverbs 8:26 to "the highest part of the dust of the earth" may be a reference to the meteoritic and other dust particles that exist throughout the lower atmosphere, and that serve as a sort of hydrological catalyst in inducing the condensation of water vapor into minute opaque particles of liquid water, which form clouds (or fog if near the ground).

However, even after their formation as clouds, the particles of water remain aloft, seemingly in complete defiance of the law of gravity. The agency that holds them up is the strong upward rush of the same air currents that caused their condensation, overbalancing the weight of the water particles until the smaller particles coalesce into sufficiently large particles to fall in spite of the strong upward currents.

All of this is a most marvelous evidence of the infinite skill and wisdom of the Creator. If it were not for this particular provision, once the temperature permitted it, all of the water in the cloud would condense and precipitate at once, in a great, destructive mass. It was a very fitting question that Elihu asked Job 3500 years ago: "Dost thou know the balancing of the clouds, the wondrous works of him which is perfect in knowledge?" Even with all the knowledge of modern science the answer to that question is still far from complete. Consider also Job's statement (Job 26:8): "He bindeth up the waters in his thick clouds; and the cloud is not rent under them."

Finally, when conditions become right, the small particles of water in the clouds (each averaging something like 1/100 inch in diameter) combine with other particles until they become of sufficient size to overcome the dynamic force of the uprushing air and to fall to the earth as rain (or snow or hail, depending on temperature and updraft conditions). The average raindrop is about 1/10 inch in diameter. "By watering, he wearieth the thick cloud" (Job 37:11).

Such passages in the Bible as the following indicate a quite modern point of view on the problem of precipitation:

Psalm 135:7. "He causeth the vapours to ascend from the ends of the earth; he maketh lightnings for the rain; he bringeth the wind out of his treasuries."

Job 28:24-27. "For he looketh to the ends of the earth, and seeth under the whole heaven, to make the weight for the winds; and he weigheth the waters by measure. When he made a decree for the rain, and a way for the lightning of the thunder: Then did he see it, and declare it. . . ."

But the amazing way in which the Bible has mapped the hydrologic cycle does not even stop here.

After the rain has fallen upon the ground, a part of it will percolate into the ground to become groundwater. This portion may be tapped by wells, may come out in springs, or may be used by plants, but most of it flows slowly through the pores in the soil or rocks toward the handiest surface drain. Some of the falling water is used directly by the plants upon which it falls, some evaporates again, and a large part runs off over the surface to the nearest river or tributary. It is this stage of the hydrologic cycle, in its various aspects, that is of most interest to man, because it is here that he is directly affected by the water, whether for good or bad.

It is interesting that most of the water for precipitation does not come from land evaporation and evaporation from inland water surfaces, as thought only a few decades ago. Quite extensive upper-air soundings of temperature, pressure, humidity, and wind, carried out within the last two or three decades by the United States Department of Agriculture have demonstrated rather conclusively that oceanic areas are the only significant sources of moisture for precipitation on continents.

In the light of all this, how significant does Solomon's statement in Ecclesiastes 1:7 appear! Immediately after his marvelously scientific statement concerning the wind circuits of the world, he completes an amazingly precise description of the hydrologic cycle in the following words: "All the rivers run into the sea; yet the sea is not full; unto the place from whence the rivers come, thither they return again."

Scientists are fond of the great precision of their measuring technique and instruments, their carefully thought-out and mathematically analyzed theories and formulas. But compared to the inimitable precision of God's creation in all its parts, the finest efforts of man are but clumsy bunglings.

The present balance between land and water, between air and water, the distance of the earth from the sun, the constituents of the atmosphere, the location of mountain ranges and equatorial ocean streams, and many other things that contribute to the workings of the hydrologic cycle, all are well known to be so delicately adjusted that any great change in their present relations would result in making life intensely uncomfortable, if not altogether impossible, upon the earth.

Thus, Isaiah's testimony (40:12) is particularly appropriate: "God hath measured the waters in the hollow of His hand, and meted out heaven with the span, and comprehended the dust of the earth in a measure, and weighed the mountains in scales, and the hills in a balance."

How thrilling it is also to realize that the writers of the Bible, under the guidance of the Spirit of God, very often refer to the precious liquid and its uses, its value, its beneficent provision at the hand of God. Often, too, physical water is used to symbolize some great spiritual reality. The Word of God itself, in its cleansing and purifying power, is typified by water in such verses as Ephesians 5:26: "That (Christ) might sanctify and cleanse (the church) with the washing of water by the Word."

The regenerating power of God in Christ, through the Holy Spirit, is often spoken of as "living water" and "water of life." In fact, it was Christ Himself who said "Except a man be born of water and the Spirit, he cannot enter into the kingdom of God" (John 3:5).

III

CREATION AND DELUGE[1]

The apparent teaching of the Bible is that all things in the physical universe were created by God during a period of six days, after which all creative activity ceased.

The date of the Creation, based on the acceptance of the genealogies in Genesis at face value, is on the order of magnitude of around six thousand years ago.[2] Subsequent to the Creation, the Bible teaches the Flood at the time of Noah destroyed all dry land inhabitants of the earth, except those in the ark, and evidently resulted in profound changes in the earth's physiography and meteorology. With reference to natural physical phenomena, then, the present order appears to date only from the time of the Deluge.

On the other hand, the commonly accepted system of historical geology teaches a gradual evolution of the earth and its inhabitants over a period of some four or five billion years. It is believed that this evolution was brought about by means of natural laws and processes such as continue at present. Creation, if such it may be called, is thus still going on. There is no place in this orthodox geology for a great world Deluge of the character described in the Bible and it is therefore ignored in standard geology textbooks.

A number of theories have been offered by Christian scholars as possible means of harmonizing the Biblical account with the accepted historical geology. It will be shown, however, that none of these harmonizations is Scripturally tenable, and that the Biblical account must be taken — if at all — in its literal sense only: namely, that the world was recently created in six literal days, by processes entirely outside the scope of nature's present order. Further, there has been at least one great discontinuity in the natural processes existing since the Creation, at the time of the Great Flood.

---

[1]Reprinted, with minor revisions, from *His*, January 1954.

[2]This figure is subject to reasonable increase. Ussher's chronology was based upon direct descent, although in some instances the Hebrew expression "begat" may refer to grandsons or even more remote descent. However, such possible gaps in the chronologies of Genesis 5 and 11 can only be stretched a reasonable amount without the record becoming irrelevant and meaningless. A date of about 15,000 B.C. for man's creation would probably represent the outside limit to which such gaps could be stretched.

Ruin-and-Reconstruction Theory

One theory which attempts to reconcile the Biblical account with historical geology is that the greater part of the geologic ages may be placed between the first and second verses of Genesis. The six days which follow are therefore a ruined earth's reconstruction rather than days of Creation. Some of the very weighty objections to this theory are briefly as follows:

1. It is explicitly contradicted by the explanatory clause of the fourth Commandment: "For in six days the Lord made heaven and earth, the sea, and all that in them is, and rested the seventh day" (Exodus 20:11).

This statement obviously refers to the summary of the account of creation as given in Genesis 2:1, 2. Its scope quite clearly is worldwide, and specifically is said to include everything *in* the earth. The geologic strata and the fossils, which are now certainly *in* the earth, must therefore be included, having been composed of materials which originally were made *during* the six days, and not *before* the six days. The fossils were not, of course, themselves made during the six days of creation, but the physical and biologic materials which eventually were to be deposited in the fossiliferous strata, must have been originally formed then.

2. The Bible teaches plainly that sin and death entered this earth only as a result of Adam's sin. (See I Corinthians 15:21; Romans 8:20-22; Romans 5:12.) This contradicts the theory that the fossil remains of millions of dead creatures, including manlike beings, date from before the creation of Adam and his subsequent Fall.

3. No worldwide geologic catastrophe such as the theory requires is found in the historical geology which the theory attempts to adopt. Many fossils, attributed by the theory to pre-Adamic ages, including human fossils, are practically identical with modern plants and animals. The theory thus requires a worldwide geologic catastrophe and extinction of all forms of life, then re-creation of many of those same forms. There is no evidence for this either in geology or the Bible. The "pre-Adamite" men which lived in the ages before the supposed catastrophe must have lived and died without a Saviour, and God's first creation therefore must have been an utter failure, if this theory is true.

4. No passage of Scripture anywhere plainly and unequivocally teaches the ruin theory. The few passages that have been offered as possibly implying a ruin and reconstruction of the earth before Adam can easily be shown to yield other and preferable interpretations. The theory has assumed the supposed ruin to be the result of Satan's sin in rebelling against God. This rebellion, however, evidently occurred in Heaven and not on this planet. No-

where in Scripture is there any statement that Satan was associated with this planet before the creation of man. According to Ezekiel 28:16, 17, he was only "cast to the earth," and "out of the mountain of God" *after* his rebellion and defeat in Heaven. See also Luke 10:18.

5. None of the standard translations of Genesis 1:2 renders the verse as: "The earth *became* waste and void" as the theory requires. The verb is the regular Hebrew verb of being, *hayetha*. In only six of its 264 occurrences in the Pentateuch is it rendered "became." There is at least one other word (*haphak*) that would have been better used here if the idea of a change from some previously different state was to be conveyed. However, even if "became" were taken as the best translation here, the only legitimate meaning of the statement would be that of the earth taking on a certain initial aspect in response to the creative fiat of God. If it be said that an initial formless and void condition for the earth would be incongruous in a "perfect" creation, it should be noted that such an objection would apply, if at all, to the creation at any stage other than its completed form. The creation was not "perfect," in the sense that it was "finished" until it *was* finished, at the end of six days, but each step was undoubtedly perfect, in God's judgment, for its immediate purpose.

6. The Hebrew words for "create" (*bara*) and for "make" (*asah*) are very often used quite interchangeably in Scripture, at least when God is the one referred to as creating or making. Therefore, the fact that *bara* is used only three times in Genesis 1 (vv. 1, 21, and 27) certainly does not imply that the other creative acts, in which "made" or some similar expression is used, were really only acts of restoration. For example, in Genesis 1:21, God "created" the fishes and birds; in 1:25, He "made" the animals and creeping things. In verse 26, Gods speaks of "making" man in His own image. The next verse states that God "created" man in His own image. No scientific or exegetical ground exists for distinction between the two processes, except perhaps a matter of grammatical emphasis. The materials which God used to "make" or "form" various things were materials which He had "created" (described in verse 1, probably). The natural reading of the whole account surely conveys the understanding of real creation throughout, with no intimation that the actual story is one of reconstruction of a devastated world. Finally, the summary verse (Genesis 2:3) clearly says that *all* of God's works, both of "creating" and "making," were completed with the six days, after which God "rested."

7. The chief proof-text for the theory, Isaiah 45:18, which says that "God created the earth not in vain (Heb. *tohu*, same word as "without form" in Genesis 1:2), can easily be understood without any reference to a hypothetical ruin of the primeval

earth. The adjective *tohu* has a variety of meanings, as determined by the particular context. In its twenty occurrences in the Old Testament, it is translated no less than ten different ways. The most common are "vanity" and "vain" (four occurrences each). In the context of Isaiah 45:18 (which has nothing whatever to do with a supposed pre-Adamic catastrophe), "in vain" is obviously the proper translation. That is, God created the earth not without a purpose — to be forever empty and formless — but rather He formed it with the intent that it would be inhabited.

Creation Day — Geologic Age Theory

The most popular theory of attempted harmonization is probably the day-age theory, according to which the creation "days" are to be understood as meaning indefinitely long ages. Those who hold this view maintain that there is a certain correspondence between the order of accepted historical geology and the order of creation in Genesis. The theory is undoubtedly attractive as a means of preventing conflict with evolutionary geologists, but it has many apparently insuperable difficulties, some of which are briefly given below:

1. The supposed correspondence between the order of Creation in Genesis and that in historical geology evaporates upon inspection of details. Thus:

a. The Bible states that all plants, even fruit trees, were made on the third day, while fish and other marine organisms were created on the fifth day. Geology reverses this order.

b. The Bible states that birds were created on the same day as fish and other marine creatures. Paleontology, however, teaches that birds were evolved from reptiles long after the origin of fish and probably even after the first appearance of mammals.

c. The Bible states that the "creeping things" (including the insects — note Leviticus 11:21) were among the last things created, coincident with land animals and reptiles. According to geology, insects appeared very early and reached their greatest development during the Carboniferous period, which preceded the appearance of reptiles, birds and mammals.

d. The Bible states that woman was created subsequent to man, and out of man. According to paleontology, the male and female of every creature, including man, must have developed and co-existed simultaneously since their first appearance.

e. The first, second, and fourth creative "days" (half of the entire period of creation) were of such nature as to leave necessarily no geological indications of their boundaries or existence.

f. The Bible states that God made the sun, moon, and stars,

on the fourth day (or at least constituted them in their positions and functions with respect to the earth), after the creation of plants on the third day. Vegetation could not exist, of course, for a long period without sunlight. No other geologically satisfactory solution to this difficulty has apparently been offered.

g. Even where the general order is not definitely inharmonious, there is such overlapping that no genuine harmony is possible. For even the merest appearance of harmony, the creative "days" must be taken as varying extremely, usually overlapping each other, and with the seventh "day" still continuing.

h. The very nebulous general agreement which may appear to exist between the Genesis and geological accounts is itself only to be expected, and therefore has no evidential value. Orthodox geology is essentially evolutionary in its structure, and thus requires a general order from simple to complex and from inorganic to organic. Similarly, it is eminently reasonable that God would proceed in Creation in the general direction of lower orders to higher. The present natural order of things is one of deterioration, in accordance with the second law of thermodynamics. During the Creation, when matter and energy were being created, this present law of nature would not have been in operation, and it would be expected that the history of Creation would be in the nature of a process of "building-up."

2. A further objection to the day-age theory involves the problem of physical evil in the world, especially death. Geology implies that pain, suffering, disease, and death have existed since the very beginning of life on earth. In fact, such things as these are regarded as basic to the evolutionary process, leading to natural selection and survival of the fittest. Thus, according to geology, suffering and death contributed to bringing man into the world. But the Bible teaches emphatically that, rather, man brought suffering and death into the world through his sin, resulting in the curse of God upon the whole creation, which "groaneth and travaileth in pain together until now."

3. God pronounced His completed creation, "everything that He had made," to be "very good" (Genesis 1:31). If the day-age theory is correct, this would mean that He could look into the rocks of the earth, see the records of millions of years of struggle, suffering, disease, famine, cruelty, pain, storm, flood, and death — indeed, He would have seen the millions of creatures entombed as fossils which now form the basis of the historical geology with which we are trying to "harmonize" the Bible — and then with evident complete satisfaction, judge it all to be "very good." Such an interpretation would appear to make God to be the "author of confusion" and a sadistic God, rather than One of order and perfection, a "God of all grace."

4. The work during the first five days of Creation was primarily to prepare the world for the occupancy of man, under whose "dominion" was to be placed "every living thing that moveth upon the earth" (Genesis 1:28). But if historical geology is correct, the overwhelming majority of all types of living things were extinct ages before man was on the scene. How could they be said to be under the dominion of man? Further, how could Adam be said to have observed and named all the birds and mammals that God had formed (Genesis 2:19) if most of them were extinct before Adam arrived? Still further, if the purpose of the other creative acts was simply to prepare the world for man, as the Bible plainly implies, what possible purpose can be found in the creation, long existence and final extinction of so many different kinds of creatures? Why this age-long spectacle of struggle and death? How could it conceivably have been necessary or even sensible, to occupy long aeons of time in an almost unimaginably slow, tortuous drama of evolution in order to accomplish God's ultimate purpose in the creation and redemption of man? No wonder most evolutionary paleontologists do not believe in a personal, purposeful God!

5. The Sabbath was instituted by God as a memorial of His completed creation, but according to uniformitarians creation, in the sense of evolutionary change is still going on, just as it has throughout geologic time. The Sabbath thus becomes quite meaningless under the day-age theory. The difficulty is increased by the fact that a "week" composed of seven aeons, each of different and indefinite length, some overlapping, some concurrent, one still continuing, could never be reasonably taken as the basis for the very rigidly described and enforced week of seven days with its Sabbath. But the creation week is definitely the basis for our week, according to the Bible.

6. The wording of the fourth Commandment plainly refutes the period theory: "Remember the Sabbath day to keep it holy. Six days shalt thou labor and do all thy work: But the seventh day is the Sabbath of the Lord thy God: For in six days the Lord made heaven and earth, the sea, and all that in them is, and rested the seventh day: wherefore the Lord blessed the Sabbath day and hallowed it" (Exodus 20:8-11).

In this passage the word "day" or "days" (Hebrew *yom* or *yamim*) appears six times. Four times the word's meaning is undoubtedly literal. The other two uses have to do with creative days; the same word is used, with no intimation that any other than the literal meaning is involved. To invest a word with symbolic meaning under such circumstances would constitute misuse of language, a crude pun at best! Remember that this Commandment was written with the finger of God Himself!

Furthermore, the word *yamim*, translated "days," is used twice in this passage, once for the six work days of God, once for the six work days of man. The word is *never* used by Moses anywhere else to mean anything other than literal days, nor evidently by any other Old Testament writer, although it occurs more than 700 times. If the "days" of Exodus 20:11 are actually "ages," then this constitutes a unique use of the word, and again without any explanatory material whatever.

7. In the relatively rare occurrences of the Hebrew singular *yom* where it is meant to refer to an indefinite period of time rather than the literal meaning of "day" (a 24-hour period, or the day-light portion thereof), such a symbolic meaning is always clear from the context. But a straightforward reading of the Genesis account does not indicate any indefinite period. Rather, it seems that it would have been practically impossible to convey to the reader the idea of literal 24-hour days of Creation any better than in the phraseology actually employed. In addition, it may be noted specifically that whenever *yom* is limited or modified by a numeral or ordinal, as is frequently the case in these passages, it always has the literal meaning. Such cases are not infrequent, occurring more than a hundred times in the Pentateuch alone. Out of all the hundreds of examples, only three possible exceptions to this rule might be claimed, (Zechariah 3:9; 14:7; Hosea 6:2). Each of these latter passages is contained in a prophecy, and each could well be interpreted in accordance with a literal meaning for "day." In view of the apparently matter-of-fact histories (not prophecies) in the Creation account, these questionable exceptions to the rule surely afford no warrant for taking the Genesis days symbolically. The Hebrew word *olam* (meaning "age," "long, indefinite time,") should have been used instead of *yom* if a long period of time were intended, or else the writer should have made it clear that *yom* was being used figuratively.

8. God actually *defined* the word "day" when He created light on the first day of Creation, and called the light "day" and the darkness "night." Whatever doubt may exist about the source of light for the first three days, there is no room for reasonable doubt as to their approximate length. It is obvious that each day did not consist of an age of light and then an age of darkness. Since all six days of Creation are spoken of in the same terms they must all be of the same character, whether literal or symbolic. And after the work of the fourth day, when doubt no longer exists concerning the source of the light for the following days, and in view of the definition of "day" as given on the first day (as well as in view of the ordinary meaning the word would be expected to impart to the readers for whom the Creation account was in-

tended), it necessarily follows that the days were meant to be understood as literal days. This conclusion is emphasized by consideration of the actual description of the work of the fourth day, when the great lights were established. In verses 1:14-19, where this work is described, the word "day" or "days" appears five times. In four of these, there is no question but that the literal meaning is intended. No sensible writer, much less an inspired writer, would use a word to mean what it customarily means several times in one paragraph, and then suddenly use it to mean something entirely different, without any explanation or clarification. The Bible is perspicuous.

9. The day-age theory cannot explain the reference to evening and morning at the end of each day's work, which seems unequivocally intended to refer to 24-hour days, and the light and dark aspects of them. Surely it is a gross misuse of language to understand "evening" as representing the beginning of an age, and "morning" its end, or any similar interpretation. The words "evening" (Hebrew *ereb*) and "morning" (*boqer*) are used more than a hundred times each in the Old Testament, and never in any other place are used in such a figurative sense as would here be required if the days which they bound are not literal days.

Variants of the Day-Age Theory

Several scholars, recognizing the fact that the "days" of the Creation record can only reasonably be understood as literal days, yet not wishing to question the supposed geological history of evolution-creation, have sought to modify the day-age theory by various means.

One such device proposes that the Creation narrative consists of a series of visions, each vision corresponding to an apparent creative day. But although revelation in Scripture is frequently in the form of visions, especially in connection with prophecy, such visions are always clearly evident as such, so that the reader immediately recognizes the necessity of interpreting symbolically. But the Genesis account is written as a matter-of-fact history, with no intimation from the writer that the account is meant to be understood as a series of symbolic visions.

A variant of the vision theory is that the Creation record was recorded on six tablets, possibly by Adam himself, at the dictation of God. Thus, it is supposed to represent what God said on each of six days of revelation. There may be truth in the idea that God revealed the Creation narrative to man at a very early date, and that it possibly was recorded on tablets in the style of other ancient writings. However, this is hardly evidence that the Genesis account merely records the revelation rather than the actual history of Creation. The best refutation of this theory appears to be a simple reading of the Genesis record. The natural reading of the narrative of each day's work certainly gives the impression that the concluding summary: "And the evening and the morning were the . . . day," refers to the creative work of the day, and not merely the work of making the day's tablet, as the theory requires.

Another theory that has been suggested is that the Creation days represent breaks between the geologic ages, days in which God performed special creative works, each day then being followed by long ages of slow development in the style of orthodox historical geology. This theory also requires a very unnatural reading of the Creation record, which is apparently continuous and is meant to describe the Creation of "heaven and earth, the sea, and all that in them is." Nor does the theory at all harmonize with orthodox geology. The geologic record often reveals gaps, sudden beginnings, etc., but these characteristics are far more frequent of occurrence, and more uniformly spread over geologic time than could possibly be harmonized with the idea of six great creative interjections into geologic history.

These and similar modifications of the basic day-age theory, although in some degree they appear to avoid difficulties inherent in the attempt to work out a real correspondence between the days of Genesis and the ages of geology, are nevertheless still subject to most of the same criticisms as the basic theory. These need not be reviewed here, but could quickly be demonstrated as equally applicable to all the various forms of the day-age theory. In any form, it appears quite inadequate as a means of bringing the Creation record into harmony with orthodox historical geology.

Many evangelical expositors in recent years have gone to the extreme of insisting that the Creation record need not be interpreted in terms of history or science at all; that is, the first few chapters of Genesis are to be understood allegorically, or poetically, rather than historically. Genesis I merely tells us that God is the Creator, but does not tell us anything about the actual historical order of creation. This type of exegesis, however, is presumptuous and dangerous, to say the least. It divests these very important records of any real meaning or significance. This method could obviously be used to emasculate any portion of the Bible which, for one reason or another, was objectionable to the reader. Most seriously, it charges the New Testament writers (note Romans 5:12-19; I Corinthians 15:21, 22, 45-47; Luke 3:38, Jude 14; etc.), and even Christ Himself (Matthew 19:3-6) with either credulity or duplicity, since they plainly taught that Adam and the events of Genesis 1-3 were genuinely historical.

Recent Creation in Six Days

The only really legitimate interpretation of the Creation record which fits the description in Genesis is apparently the literal one, namely that Creation took place in six literal days. The Bible says that God "rested" after the six days; the "works were finished from the foundation of the world" (Hebrews 4:3). The processes used by God in Creation are therefore not now in operation, and thus cannot be studied in terms of present physical laws and phenomena. The principle of uniformity, however valid it may be at present, cannot be applied to the six days of Creation. It is therefore not surprising that a historical geology built upon this principle, and purporting to give an account of the origins of the earth and its inhabitants, is found to be contradictory to the revealed record of Creation. Since Creation was accomplished by entirely different processes than we can now study scientifically, it is clear that the only way we can know anything definitely about Creation is by means of God's revelation concerning it. This revelation He has given us in the Bible, and it teaches as plainly as could possibly be put into the few words devoted to the subject the fact of the creation of all things in six literal days. All theories of attempted harmonization of the Biblical account with orthodox geology require such juggling of the plain sense of the account so as in effect to amount to its rejection, with the implication that the Holy Spirit was unable to say what He meant to say, and that therefore His record must now be corrected according to our better understanding of Creation as discovered through the study of geology.

Was the Flood Worldwide?

If the Biblical record of Creation is true, the fossil-bearing rocks of the earth must have been formed subsequent to the Fall of man and the introduction of death and decay into the world by God's Curse on the whole Creation (Genesis 3:17-19; Romans 8:20-22). Therefore, these geologic strata must be explained largely on the basis of catastrophism, rather than uniformity. This immediately brings to mind the Deluge at the time of Noah, which is the greatest physiographic event recorded in Scripture or in human history, and which can be seen to have had tremendous geologic implications.

Since a number of harmonizers of the Bible with geology have sought to show that the Flood was only a local inundation in the Tigris-Euphrates region, it will first be necessary to establish the clear Biblical teaching of a worldwide Flood. Consider, for example, the following very cogent reasons for understanding the Scriptural account of the Deluge to have certain reference to a universal cataclysm:

1. The expressions of universality in the account (Genesis 6-9) are not confined to one or two verses, but are repeated in various ways more than a score of times, the writer apparently guarding by every means possible against this very theory that the Flood might be only a limited inundation.

2. There are numerous references to the Flood in later parts of Scripture, all plainly indicating that the writers regarded the account in worldwide terms. The Lord Jesus Christ (Matthew 24:37-39; Luke 17:26, 27) makes the worldwide judgment of the Deluge to be a type of His own return in judgment upon this present world.

3. The record makes it plain that the waters overtopped the mountains which even in the vicinity of the Tigris-Euphrates region reach great heights. The mountains of Ararat contain peaks over fifteen thousand feet high. The waters "prevailed upon the earth" at least 150 days, so that waters which covered mountains in one region of the world must necessarily have attained to similar elevations in all other parts of the world.

4. The primary purpose of the Flood was to "destroy all flesh" and especially to destroy man from the earth. During the years before the Flood (perhaps 1600), conditions were evidently favorable to abundant procreation. The idea that man could only have spread over a small region during this period is quite unreasonable and certainly could not be said to harmonize with anthropology. Consequently, the geographical extent of the Flood would have to be worldwide.

5. The purpose of the Ark was to "keep seed alive upon the face of all the earth," but this purpose was entirely superficial and unreasonable if the only life that was destroyed was within a certain limited area. The Ark had a carrying capacity at least equal to that of 500 ordinary cattle cars, far too large for the needs of merely a small region.

6. Most important, the entire Biblical record of the Flood becomes almost ridiculous if it is conceived in terms of a local flood. The whole procedure of constructing a great boat, involving a tremendous amount of work, can hardly be described as anything but utterly foolish and unnecessary. How much more sensible it would have been for God merely to have warned Noah of the coming destruction, so that he could have moved to another region to which the flood would not reach. The great numbers of animals of all kinds, and certainly the birds (which migrate vast distances), could easily have moved out also, without having had to be stored and tended for a year in the Ark! The entire

story thus becomes little more than nonsense if it is taken as a mere local flood in Mesopotamia.

Geologic Implications of the Flood

If such an event has actually occurred in recent times, with flood waters covering the entire world for almost a year, and even the mountain tops for perhaps nine months, it is ridiculous to ignore such a phenomenon when attempting to develop a valid historical geology. Some legitimate geologic inferences that may be drawn from the Biblical record of the Deluge are as follows:

1. There were great volcanic and tectonic disturbances, and great quantities of juvenile water (i.e., water which emerged for the first time from the earth's crust to become part of the earth's surface waters) poured out on the earth. This is the reasonable implication of statements made concerning the breaking up of the fountains of the great deep (Genesis 7:11; 8:2).

2. Antediluvian meteorological conditions were quite different in character from those now prevailing. Otherwise, it would have been quite impossible for rain to have fallen continuously for forty days and forty nights all around the world, especially in such torrential fashion that it was described as the "flood-gates" (A. V. "windows") of Heaven being opened. The tremendous amounts of water implied are not possible under present atmospheric conditions. Other evidences of pre-Deluge climatological differences from the present include the references to the early non-existence of rainfall (2:5); the "waters above the firmament" (not "in the firmament," therefore not the clouds, 1:7); and the postdiluvian introduction of the rainbow (9:13). These conditions described in the Bible add weight to the evidence that the principle of uniformity cannot be applied to the Deluge or to the antediluvian period.

3. The great volumes of water which were thus turned loose on the earth, both from the "fountains of the great deep" and from the "flood-gates of Heaven" must, of absolute necessity, have accomplished a vast amount of geologic work in a relatively short period. The Bible also speaks of the waters "going and returning continually" (Genesis 8:3), then of "the mountains rising and the valleys sinking, with the waters hasting away" (Psalm 104:6-9 A.S.V.), and of the waters "overturning the earth" (Job 12:15). Erosion and resedimentation must have taken place on a gigantic scale. Previous isostatic adjustments, of whatever sort they were, must have been entirely unbalanced by the great complex of hydrostatic and hydrodynamic forces unleashed in the floodwaters,

resulting very likely in great telluric movements. Associated with the volcanic phenomena and the great rains must also have been tremendous tidal effects, windstorms, and a great complexity of currents, cross-currents, whirlpools, and other hydraulic phenomena. After the flood-gates were restrained, and the fountains of the deep stopped, for a long time much more geologic work must have been accomplished as the masses of water were settling into new basins and the earth was adjusting itself to new physiographic and hydrologic balances.

4. Since the Flood was said to have killed "every living substance upon the face of the ground," and in view of the great masses of sediment being moved back and forth and finally deposited by the flood-waters, it would be expected that great numbers of plants and animals would be buried by the sediments, under conditions eminently favorable to preservation and fossilization. Conditions for extensive fossil production could never have been so favorable as during the Deluge. Since the Deluge was worldwide and recent, this can only mean that many, probably most, of the fossils that are now found in earth's sedimentary rock beds were entombed there during the Flood.

5. Finally, it may very fairly be inferred from the record that it would now be impossible to discern geologically much of the earth's history prior to the Flood, at least on the assumption of continuity with present conditions. Whatever geologic deposits may have existed before the Flood must have been almost completely eroded, reworked, and redeposited during the Flood, perhaps several times. Such geologic time-clocks as we may be able to use to date events subsequent to the Flood cannot therefore legitimately be used to extend chronologies into antediluvian time. The basic premise of all such chronometers is uniformity and, if the Flood record be true, the premise of uniformity is, at that point at least, false.

Geologic Implications of Creation

The record of Creation in Genesis reveals that the world was created complete and full-grown during the six days of Creation. Adam was created as a grown man, with every appearance of having been growing and developing for a score or more years. So with Eve. The only way of denying this is to deny the reliability of the Scripture which teaches it. Similarly, the birds and animals were created, not in germinal form, but full-grown. Plants also were created full-grown, with trees already bearing fruit, and not as seeds. The biological world, with all its interrelationships, was therefore created full-grown. And this implies that the soil in which the plants were to grow was already formed. Similarly, the ocean also contained most of its salts and various chemicals for the marine organisms that were created for it. And so on. All the innumerable and complex interrelationships between the plant and animal kingdoms, the organic and inorganic realms, must have been created as a going concern at the time of Creation. God created a functioning universe. This can only mean that the earth and its inhabitants gave many appearances of age the very moment they were created. Consequently, geo-chronometric methods which assume that apparent age necessarily means real age, as all such methods do assume, must apply the principle of uniformity not only since the end of Creation (and even this application is invalid in the light of the Deluge, as we have seen), but also since the very beginning of Creation, thus in effect denying the fact that a real Creation could ever have taken place, and patently denying the truth of God's revelation of Creation.

The commonly expressed notion that, since God cannot lie, He cannot create something with an appearance of age, ignores the fact that God has given us His own revelation about the events of Creation. The assumption is then made of a uniform and continuous operation of the processes of nature then and now. Since Creation was accomplished by entirely different processes than now operate in nature, it is presumptuous for man to attempt to deduce the history of Creation on the basis of present processes. Revelation is necessary, and God has supplied it to us. Any contradiction between this account and man's interpretation of geologic history is not the result of God's deceptive Creation of apparent age, but rather man's rejection (or allegorization) of God's revelation concerning true ages and origins.

Much important geologic work was undoubtedly accomplished during the six days of Creation, especially the first three. This work could not be determined now on the basis of uniformity. Similarly, the strong implication of the account of the first and fourth days of Creation is that the astronomical universe was created full-grown. Theories about the evolution of galactic systems, etc., particularly when used as chronometers, must become for the Christian very questionable when they begin to contradict this revealed fact.

The Principle of Uniformity

In view of all the above facts, it is necessary to conclude that the geologic principle of uniformity would not have been in operation during at least two extremely important periods of earth history, the Creation and the Deluge. Thus the Bible, and not the present, is the key to the past.

This is a very important fact, because the entire structure of evolutionary historical geology rests squarely upon the assumption of uniformity, and the scientific basis of the theory of evolution is almost entirely grounded on the testimony of historical geology. And in turn the theory of evolution has been made the basis of all the godless philosophies that are plaguing the world today and in particular is the spearhead of attack against Biblical Christianity.

A great need exists today for scientifically trained Christians to re-study the data of geology, with the goal of developing a true science of historical geology based, as it must be, on the acceptance at full face value of the two great truths of a real and recent Creation, and a universal Deluge, two events which were accomplished by means largely or entirely inoperative in the present system of nature. Only then can a true science of historical geology be developed and a self-consistent Christian apologetic in this field be given.

It is apparently of our day that Peter speaks (II Peter 3:3-6): "There shall come in the last days scoffers, walking after their own lusts, and saying, Where is the promise of His coming? For since the fathers fell asleep, all things continue as they were from the beginning of the creation. For this they willingly are ignorant of, that by the word of God the heavens were of old, and the earth standing out of the water and in the water: Whereby the world that then was, being overflowed with water, perished."

The modern doctrine of uniformity, with both its fruits (denial of miracles and the coming judgment at the return of Christ), and its apparent scientific basis (the willful rejection of the two great revealed facts of a real Creation and a subsequent world-destroying Deluge) are, with penetrating lucidity, given in this remarkable prophecy. It is high time that Christians heeded it, instead of defending the very teachings that it condemns.

IV

THE POWER OF THE WORD[1]

Christians often speak, and rightly so, of the power of the Word of God, thinking of such a text as Hebrews 4:12: "For the word of God is quick (i.e., "living"), and powerful, and sharper than any two-edged sword, piercing even to the dividing asunder of soul and spirit, and of the joints and marrow, and is a discerner of the thoughts and intents of the heart." There are numerous illustrations in Scripture, and in the life of every soul-winning Christian, of the power of the Word of God to convict and to illumine the mind and heart of a lost man and to bring him to Christ.

Power and the Word of God

But it is not often realized how intimately associated is the concept of the power of God, not only in the spiritual sense but even in the physical realm, with the Word of God. Of course, the term "the word of God" is used in more than one sense in Scripture. It is used of the Scriptures themselves, the written Word. It is also used to refer to any form of communication from God to man, whereby God reveals Himself to man, whether by an audible voice, by vision, through conscience, or even in the phenomena of nature. And it is one of the great titles of the Lord Jesus Christ Himself, as the living Word of God, the One through whom God has been most clearly and completely revealed to man, in all the perfection of His love. But wherever the term is used, it brings to view in some way the fact that God is speaking and making Himself known in man's experience.

The Word of His Power. In Hebrews 1:3, we have a striking intimation that God's Word is associated with physical power. The first two verses of Hebrews bring to view both the written Word and the living Word: "God, who at sundry times and in divers manners spake in time past unto the fathers by the prophets, hath in these last days spoken unto us by His Son."

Then the tremendous assertion is made not only that the Son, the living Word, "made the worlds," but also that He is "upholding all things by the word of His power," that is, that all the matter and physical phenomena of the universe are being sustained by "the word of His power."

---

[1]Based on an article in *Bibliotheca Sacra,* January, 1959.

The striking implications of this verse could only have been understood (and then only in very slight degree) in recent decades, when it has been discovered that everything in the physical universe is basically and fundamentally energy. All phenomena that affect the senses — such as light, sound, heat, etc., as well as matter itself — are merely different forms of energy. Thus, energy is measured by the ability to perform mechanical "work," and all natural processes involve utilization of energy in some form. Einstein formulated the equation that describes the equivalence of matter and energy which, as is well known, has served as the basis of modern revolutionary discoveries in the field of nuclear energy. Matter, composed of molecules, atoms, electrons, protons, neutrons, and numerous submicroscopic particles, is now known to be nothing really substantial at all but composed fundamentally of tremendous energy. When some of this energy is released, either through nuclear fission or thermo-nuclear fusion, the physical effects are also tremendous. The still mysterious "binding energy" that normally holds the atom together in opposition to the tremendous forces that are always acting to disintegrate it, is apparently somehow related to the primal and basic energy of creation.

Energy can manifest its presence in different phenomena, depending upon the nature and velocities of the motions which embody it. Whether it appears as matter, or as light, heat, etc., is governed by the particular motions that occur.

And the Scripture quoted above apparently says that the Lord Jesus Christ is the ultimate Source of the infinite power (or energy) which, revealing itself through its outworking (the Word), is the agency by which all the physical universe is "upheld." Here is the modern discovery of the equivalence of matter and energy, expressed 1900 years ago, and further teaching that it is the living Word of God which supplies the power for keeping the matter of the universe from disintegrating, and for enabling it to manifest all the multitudinous physical phenomena that constitute God's creation.

Power in the Scriptures. There are several different Greek words which are translated in the New Testament by our English word "power," and they each give a slightly different shade of meaning, but all are legitimately included under our concept of power. And it is significant that each word is used with reference to the Word of God.

For example, one of the words is the Greek *exousia,* meaning "authority." This is the word used by the Lord Jesus in Matthew 28:18 when He said: "All power is given unto me in heaven and in earth." This is the word also which is used in Luke 4:32 which says that ". . . His word was with power."

Another Greek word frequently translated "power" is *dunamis,* from which we derive our English word "dynamic," and which means "strength" or "might." This word is found in Hebrews 1:3: ". . . the word of His power," and also, for example, in Matthew 22:29, where the "scriptures" and "the power of God" are used essentially as equal terms.

Still another very interesting Greek word is *energes*, which is the very word from which we get our English word "energy." This word is used in Hebrews 4:12, where the Word of God is said to be "quick and *powerful*." The meaning in this verse is that the Word of God is full of energy; it is *energizing*; it produces work resulting from the energy contained therein.

In the Old Testament, the word which is most frequently translated "power" is the Hebrew *koach*. In Psalm 29, the great "Psalm of the Voice of the Lord" (and, therefore, the psalm of the Word of God), verse 4 states: "The voice of the Lord is powerful; the voice of the Lord is full of majesty."

God's Word, therefore, is said to be filled with power, in both the Old and New Testaments, and by each of the major words which are used to convey the different connotations of the concept of power.

Power in Modern Science

Modern Technical Concept of Energy and Power. The concept of power or energy is extremely important in modern science and technology, and it is striking to note how our technical meaning of these terms is so similar to their meaning as given in Scripture. Energy is not a substance but is a concept meaning the property of matter or phenomena which has the capacity of performing useful work, in the moving of forces through distances – in "making the wheels go around." In fact, the term "work" is practically equivalent to "energy," each amount of work done being numerically equal to the energy expended in doing the work.

Power is a similar concept, being the rate or speed with which the energy is used or the work is performed. Our familiar unit of horsepower, for example, represents 550 foot-pounds of energy being used up each second. (A foot-pound is the amount of work required to lift a one-pound weight a distance of one foot.)

This concept of energy is of absolutely paramount importance in all of the great modern advances in science and engineering which have contributed so immensely to modern civilization. R. B. Lindsay, Professor of Physics, Director of the Ultrasonics Laboratory, and Dean of the Graduate School at Brown University, says in a recent article:

"Of all unifying concepts in the whole field of physical science, that of energy has proved to be the most significant and useful. Not only has it played a major role in the development of science, but, by common consent, it is the physical concept which has had and still has the widest influence on human life in all its aspects."[2]

The importance of this concept of power and energy is seen in the fact that the most generally accepted definition of engineering (by engineers, at least) is that it is the "art and science by which the properties of matter and sources of power in nature are made useful to man in structures, machines and manufactured products." This study of the properties of matter (and matter is now itself a "source of power") and the sources of power has resulted in a fiftyfold increase in per capita power in our country in the past fifty years. That is, each individual person can now, on the average, accomplish fifty times as much as one could fifty years ago, by means of machines and methods developed by aid of the energy concept, and this of course is the reason for our modern high standard of living.

The Two Energy Laws. This powerful scientific concept of energy is embodied in two great laws, which are the two most basic, universal, and important laws of all science. They are known as the first and second laws of thermodynamics. The name arises from the fact that, historically, they were first discovered and proved in the study of thermodynamics, the science of heat power, but their applicability has since been proved to extend to literally every branch of human scientific knowledge. The great Harvard physicist, P. W. Bridgman, says, for example:

"The two laws of thermodynamics are, I suppose, accepted by physicists as perhaps the most secure generalizations from experience that we have. The physicist does not hesitate to apply the two laws to any concrete situation in the confidence that nature will not let him down."[3]

Probably all of the basic formulas and methods in every branch of science and engineering are ultimately either based on, or intimately related to, these two great principles.

The Law of Energy Conservation. The first law of thermodynamics is also known as the law of energy conservation and states that although energy can change forms it cannot be either created or destroyed and therefore the sum total of energy remains constant. Energy can appear in many forms, including light, heat, sound, pressure, electricity, chemical energy, mechanical energy, nuclear energy, etc., and all of these are, under the proper conditions, interchangeable. Numerical conversion factors are known, in most cases, to express the transformation of energy

---

[2]R. B. Lindsay: "Concept of Energy in Mechanics," *Scientific Monthly,* October, 1957, p. 188.

[3]P. W. Bridgman: "Reflections on Thermodynamics," *American Scientist,* October, 1953, p. 549.

from one form into another. And it is significant that all real processes in nature, as well as those invented by man, necessarily involve the utilization and transformation of energy, in order to accomplish the work involved in the processes.

But as these interchanges take place, this law insists that the total amount of energy put into the system must equal the total taken out. None of it is destroyed, nor is any new energy created in the process. This is true in any small system or process and must therefore be true for any combination of such systems, and is true for the universe as a whole. Therefore, no energy is now being created or destroyed anywhere in the universe, so far as science can know. And since matter itself is merely one form of energy, this means that creation is not taking place now at all.

This in turn leads to the conclusion that when energy was originally created the processes of creation must have been entirely different than those now being observed in the universe and that, therefore, the Creation itself cannot be studied at all by means of modern science; revelation is required.

And this is, of course, the testimony of the account of Creation in Scripture. After describing the events and sequence of Creation during the six days, the writer strongly emphasizes that the work of Creation thereupon stopped: "Thus the heavens and the earth were finished, and all the host of them. And on the seventh day God ended His work which He had made; and He rested on the seventh day from all His work which He had made. And God blessed the seventh day, and sanctified it: because that in it He had rested from all His work which God created and made" (Genesis 2:1-3).

This is the modern principle of energy conservation (perhaps, in view of the equivalence of work and energy, it would even be legitimate to paraphrase the above as "God rested from all His energy which He had made"), expressed at the very beginning of the written Word of God. This is another of the many principles and facts of modern science contained in Scripture. It is also taught in the New Testament (cf. Hebrews 4:3, 10).

Law of Energy Deterioration. The second law of thermodynamics states that in any real process or system in which energy is being transformed into other forms, at least some of it is transformed into heat energy which cannot be converted back into other useful forms. That is, although none of the energy is destroyed, some of it deteriorates and becomes less useful and available for work than it was at the beginning of the process. In a more general sense, this law expresses the fact that in any closed system there must always be a decrease of order or organization, unless external energy or intelligence is applied to counteract this trend.

Again, since the universe as a whole can be considered as an aggregation of finite systems, this law implies that there is a continual decrease of useful energy for performing the work of running the universe or, in other terms, that there is a continual increase of disorder in the universe. The universe is therefore growing old, wearing out, running down, due ultimately to burn itself out when all of its useful energy is converted to unavailable heat energy and the entire universe reaches a constant, uniform, low temperature, and ceases all its motions. At least, this is the implication of this second law of thermodynamics, unless God somehow intervenes before the deterioration is complete.

But all of this is also taught in Scripture, and is intimately connected with the Curse of God on His Creation, pronounced as a result of man's sin. Decay and even death itself are manifestations in biological processes of this energy deterioration principle. The Scriptures teach the physical aging and death of the universe, the decay principle in life processes, etc., and also teach of course that God, who established this condition is not Himself subject to it, and that in His own time He will intervene to set it aside, remove the Curse and create a new universe in which there is no deterioration, decay and death. For example, the writer of Hebrews states in quoting Psalm 102: "And, Thou, Lord, in the beginning hast laid the foundation of the earth; and the heavens are the works of Thine hands; They shall perish; but Thou remainest; and they all shall wax old as doth a garment; And as a vesture shalt Thou fold them up, and they shall be changed: but Thou art the same, and Thy years shall not fail" (Hebrews 1:10-12).

The Apostle Paul says in the classic eighth chapter of Romans: "For the creation was made subject to vanity, not willingly, but by reason of Him who hath subjected the same in hope. Because the creation itself also shall be delivered from the bondage of corruption (lit., 'decay') into the glorious liberty of the children of God. For we know that the whole creation groaneth and travaileth in pain together until now" (Romans 8:20-22).

This law, as well as teaching the necessity of future intervention by God if the world is to be spared complete deterioration, proves the fact of Creation. If the world is now growing old, it must once have been young; if it is wearing out, it once was new; before it could run down, it must have first been "wound up."

Analogies between Science and Scripture

Analogy of the Word and Physical Power. In view of the close Biblical connection between the concepts of the Word of God and the power of God, it is not surprising to find in searching the Scriptures that the effects of the Word upon the hearts of individuals are often compared to the physical phenomena associated with the various forms of energy. One might even see a relation between the fact that the originally created energy can neither be destroyed nor augmented with the revealed fact that God's written Word is likewise now completed, and is neither to be added to nor taken from (Revelation 22:18, 19; Jude 3).

There is no corresponding analogy with the second law of thermodynamics, of course, since this law represents a state of things in the physical universe resulting from the Fall and God's resulting Curse on the whole Creation. The law of energy deterioration is a continual reminder that the Creation is under the bondage of corruption, departing ever farther from its originally intended state of everlasting perfection. The Word of God, on the other hand, is completely perfect and eternally pure. "The law of the Lord is perfect . . . the testimony of the Lord is sure. . . . The statutes of the Lord are right . . . the commandment of the Lord is pure" (Psalm 19:7, 8).

The Energy of Light. The most basic of all forms of energy is light energy, including not only visible light but all forms of radiant energy, from the very short wave length rays as X-rays and cosmic rays at one extreme, to the long wave length rays manifested by heat and the electromagnetic rays used in radio and television communications. All these forms of light move in waves, at a tremendous rate of speed known as the velocity of light. Furthermore, the energy of radioactivity — whereby matter is disintegrating — and even the energy of the atom itself are also associated with light energy. The Einstein equation relates matter and energy by a simple constant, and that constant is the velocity of light.

Light energy is thus the primal form of energy, and the spiritual analogy is that, through the Word of God, the sin-darkened soul must first of all be enlightened before he can manifest any other form of spiritual energy in his life. "The entrance of Thy words giveth light" (Psalm 119:130); "For God, who commanded the light to shine out of darkness, hath shined in our hearts, to give the light of the knowledge of the glory of God in the face of Jesus Christ" (II Corinthians 4:6).

With reference to the latter verse, it is very significant that the very first creative command of God recorded in Scripture (and therefore the first mention of God speaking, i.e., of the Word of God): was that of the creation of light. "And God said, Let there be light: and there was light" (Genesis 1:3). Another very significant statement is made in Genesis 1:17 when, in describing the establishment of the sun, moon, and stars, their function was said to be "to give light upon the earth."

The light, or radiant energy coming from the sun to the earth, is now known by science to be the source of practically all of the earth's energy by which the processes of nature and life itself are maintained upon the earth. In fact, all of the earth's energy, except that of its own rotation and the atomic energy of its matter, has come originally from the sun. It has been calculated that all of the earth's energy stores — its coal, oil, and gas reserves, its timber and other burnable material, even its uranium and other fissionable atoms — could supply a total amount of power equal only to that which reaches the earth from the sun in just three days' time.[4] Truly, with respect to physical phenomena and biological life on the earth, the sun is "the light of the world."

These facts intensify the significance to us of the tremendous claim made by the Lord Jesus, the Living Word, when He said: "I am the light of the world: he that followeth me shall not walk in darkness, but shall have the light of life" (John 8:12). As the sun is the source of earth's physical energy, so He is the source of the spiritual illumination and power of the believer. The written Word is likewise said to be the source of light for the divinely energized individual. "Thy word is a lamp unto my feet, and a light unto my path" (Psalm 119:105); "We have also a more sure word of prophecy: whereunto ye do well that ye take heed, as unto a light that shineth in a dark place" (II Peter 1:19).

Atomic Energy. We have mentioned that atomic energy is itself intimately related to the energy of light. All the matter of the universe is basically energy and therefore in one sense is light energy. However, it normally appears not as light at all but as physical matter, characterized by weight, hardness, etc. This form of energy likewise was created and is sustained by the Word of God: "By the word of the Lord were the heavens made; and all the host of them by the breath of His mouth" (Psalm 33:6); "Through faith we understand that the worlds were framed by the word of God, so that things which are seen were not made of things which do appear" (Hebrews 11:3).

Not only were the worlds brought into being through the Word of God but they are sustained by His Word. Hebrews 1:3 has already been mentioned in this connection. Another very significant passage is found in II Peter 3 where, in describing the anti-supernaturalistic scoffers of the last time, Peter says: "For this they willingly are ignorant of, that by the word of God the heavens were of old, and the earth standing out of the water and in the water . . . but the heavens and the earth which are now, by the same word are kept in store, reserved unto fire against the day of judgment and perdition of ungodly men" (II Peter 3:5, 7).

---

[4]Eugene Ayres and Charles A. Scarlott: *Energy Sources*, McGraw-Hill Book Co., New York, 1952, p. 186.

The tenth verse of II Peter 3 prophesies that at the coming Day of the Lord this maintaining power of the Word of God will be withdrawn from His present activity of "holding together" (Colossians 1:17) all material things, the binding energy will be withdrawn and all the atomic structure of the earth permitted to disintegrate instantly into other forms of energy — sound, heat, and fire. "But the day of the Lord will come as a thief in the night; in the which the heavens shall pass away with a great noise, and the elements shall melt with fervent heat, the earth also and the works that are therein shall be burned up. Seeing then that all these things shall be dissolved [lit., "released," or "unloosed"], what manner of persons ought ye to be in all holy conversation and godliness, looking for and hasting unto the coming of the day of God, wherein the heavens [i.e., the atmospheric heavens], being on fire shall be dissolved, and the elements shall melt with fervent heat?" (II Peter 3:10-12).

And just as the Word of God, through atomic power, has created and maintained the structure of the physical universe, so does His Word create and sustain the spiritual life of the one who believes after receiving the light from the Word: "Being born again, not of corruptible seed, but of incorruptible, by the word of God, which liveth and abideth forever" (I Peter 1:23); "Verily, verily, I say unto you, he that heareth my word, and believeth on Him that sent me, hath everlasting life, and shall not come into condemnation; but is passed from death unto life" (John 5:24); "But He answered and said, It is written, Man shall not live by bread alone, but by every word that proceedeth out of the mouth of God" (Matthew 4:4).

The Energy of Sound and Heat. Sound is another form of energy, moving out as a wave from its source. The sound of thunder was the most awe-inspiring sound known to the Biblical writers, and was often compared to the voice of God. For example: "The voice of the Lord is upon the waters; the God of glory thundereth; the Lord is upon many waters" (Psalm 29:3).

For the one who has been illumined, redeemed, and kept by the Word of God, the energy thus imparted to his spirit must make itself manifest in a spoken witness so that through him the Word of God sounds out to others, ultimately over many waters and to the ends of the earth, in fashion analogous to the spreading of sound waves out from their source. "So then faith cometh by hearing, and hearing by the word of God. But I say, Have they not heard? Yes verily, their sound went into all the earth, and their words unto the ends of the world" (Romans 10:17, 18).

This passage is quoted by Paul from Psalm 19:4. The latter part of the verse refers to the sun and calls attention to the heat energy radiated from the sun to all the earth, providing the warmth necessary for life to be sustained. The same energy source also produces the thunder associated with the rains. Thus the heat energy from the sun is almost as important as the light energy therefrom and, of course, we have already noted that heat is really a special form of light. It is significant that in this nineteenth Psalm the mention of the sun's heat is immediately followed by mentioning the converting power of the Word of God. "His [the sun's] going forth is from the end of the heaven, and his circuit unto the ends of it: and there is nothing hid from the heat thereof. The law of the Lord is perfect, converting the soul" (Psalm 19:6, 7)

Therefore, heat energy, like sound energy, is pictured to us as analogous to the process whereby the Word of God through the testimony of Christians, both individually and corporately, is used to witness and convert. The sounded witness alone, while permitting men to hear the gospel, will not convert the soul unless presented in warmth and zeal, earnestness and sincerity. But the Word of God sent forth in the warmth of a heart of love for Christ and lost men will melt cold hearts. "He sendeth out His word, and melteth them" (Psalm 147:18).

Electrical and Chemical Energy. Since people in Biblical times knew nothing about electricity and chemistry, one might think at first that these two very important forms of power could not be mentioned in the Bible. However, they are mentioned, and once again we find that they, too, are compared to the Word of God. Electrical energy, now as well as in ancient times, appears most strikingly in the form of lightning. In Scripture both the lightning and thunder are symbols of the voice of God. "The Lord also thundered in the heavens, and the Highest gave His voice; hail stones and coals of fire. Yea, He sent out His arrows, and scattered them; and He shot out lightnings, and discomfited them" (Psalm 18:13, 14). "Hear attentively the noise of His voice, and the sound that goeth out of His mouth. He directeth it under the whole heaven, and His lightning unto the ends of the earth" (Job 37:2, 3; cf. Job 38:35).

God is thus seen to speak in the lightning to defeat and rout the enemy, like great arrows in His hand. Similarly, the Word of God is the sword of the Spirit, wielded by the Christian in resisting the devil and defeating him (cf. Ephesians 6:17; Hebrews 4:12).

Great stores of chemical energy are locked in the earth's reserves of coal, oil, peat, timber, gas, etc. This has originated from the sun's light energy which through the marvelous process of photosynthesis has caused the growth of plant life, and this in turn has been used to sustain animal life When the plants and, at least in some cases, animals too have died and been buried, the energy stored up in their cell structure has been preserved in the ground over many years.

This energy remains chained up, so to speak, until released through the process of burning to be converted into useful work. When set on fire, however, chemical energy in its various forms provides a great portion of the power used in industry and transportation. The Word of God is like this form of power, too. Says Jeremiah: "Wherefore thus saith the Lord God of Hosts, Because ye speak this word, behold, I will make my words in thy mouth fire, and this people wood, and it shall devour them" (Jeremiah 5:14); "Then I said, I will not make mention of Him, nor speak any more in His name. But His word was in mine heart as a burning fire shut up in my bones, and I was weary with forbearing, and I could not stay" (Jeremiah 20:9).

Stress and Strain: Weight. Chemical energy is one form of potential energy, in which the capacity for doing work is stored up, motionless and ineffective until released. Another type of potential energy is that contained in an elastic material which is held under restraint; that is, it has been either compressed or stretched and if released would revert to its original dimensions and accomplish work in so doing. Examples would be a compressed or elongated spring, water held behind a dam or kept under pressure in a pipe system, compressed air or steam under pressure, etc. One of the laws of physics states that the stress is proportional to the strain; that is, the amount of potential force that could be exerted by the material is directly in proportion to the amount of distortion that it has undergone. And the amount of stored energy is essentially the product of the stress and strain.

There seems to be an implication, spiritually speaking, of this form of power released by the Word in Luke 16:16, 17: "The law and the prophets were until John: since that time the kingdom of God is preached, and every man presseth into it. And it is easier for heaven and earth to pass, than one tittle of the law to fail." In this passage it is noted that as the Word is preached it exerts a pressure upon its hearers, causing them to "press" into the kingdom, or to "take it by force" according to the parallel passage in Matthew 11:12. Only when the "tension" or "pressure" resulting in the heart of the hearer of the Word is relieved by his permitting the Spirit's conviction to press him into the kingdom is he truly set "free from the law" (Romans 8:2).

Gravitational energy, which manifests itself in the weight of objects, is a related form of potential energy. It appears as the capacity of an object which has been lifted against the force of gravity to fall when released. This energy is measured by the product of the weight of the object and its height above the ground or other surface to which it could fall Similarly, the

Word of God is a great weight, burdening those who resist it. As an example, some of the Corinthian church members ridiculed the physical appearance and speech of the Apostle Paul, but his divinely inspired epistles, embodying as they did the very Word of God, were not so easily shunted aside. "For his letters, say they, are weighty and powerful; but his bodily presence is weak, and his speech contemptible" (II Corinthians 10:10).

Mechanical Energy. Most of the various forms in which energy can appear are but preparatory to the accomplishment of the work of which they are capable. Electrical energy, chemical energy, strain energy, etc., all must be converted into mechanical energy in order to accomplish the work which needs to be done. Mechanical energy is the energy of motion, the turning of wheels, the moving of loads, the driving of hammers. It is also called kinetic energy.

This energy of movement and mechanical work is implied in such passages as the following, speaking of the spiritual effects of the Word: "He sendeth forth His commandment upon earth: His word runneth very swiftly" (Psalm 147:15); "Is not my word like as a fire? saith the Lord; and like a hammer that breaketh the rock in pieces?" (Jeremiah 23:29).

The accomplishment of God's work through the Word is also taught, analogous to the way in which the physical work of the world is accomplished through the conversion of other forms of energy into the kinetic energy of useful work. "So shall my word be that goeth forth out of my mouth: it shall not return unto me void, but it shall accomplish that which I please, and shall prosper in the thing whereto I sent it" (Isaiah 55:11).

Furthermore, as has been noted, all energy is fundamentally manifested in motion. The various forms of energy basically are simply exhibiting different kinds and rates of motion. The most obvious form is the mechanical energy just mentioned, but even the primal form of energy, that of light, is associated with the ultimate in motion, that of the velocity of light which is somewhat over 186,000 miles per second.

It is significant, then, that the origin of God's Word is associated with motion. Prior to the first spoken command in Creation, when the Word of God was first heard, the Scriptures say that ". . . the Spirit of God moved upon the face of the waters." The process by which God inspired His written Word, mysterious and diversified though it may have been, was likewise fundamentally characterized by motion: "For the prophecy came not in old time by the will of man: but holy men of God spake as they were moved (lit., "carried along") by the Holy Ghost (II Peter 1:21).

Conclusion

The Eternal Word. These many analogies between the spiritual power associated with God's Word and the different forms of physical power of His universe are too numerous to be accidental. They bear a dual witness both to the divine inspiration of the Scriptures which record them and to the divine origin of the physical creation at the hand of the Author of Scripture.

And we have seen that actually this is more than an analogy. The source of the physical power of the universe is itself the Word of God, upholding all things thereby.

But there is one sense in which this resemblance is incomplete. The law of energy conservation teaches that the total energy of creation is finite and unchanging, and the law of energy deterioration teaches that the universe is growing old and wearing out. The Word of God, on the other hand, is not finite but is infinite; it has no bounds. And it is not temporal, subject to aging and decay, but is eternal.

"Forever, O Lord, thy word is settled in heaven" (Psalm 119: 89); "Heaven and earth shall pass away, but my words shall not pass away" (Matthew 24:35); "Thy word is true from the beginning (i.e., eternity past); and every one of Thy righteous judgments endureth for ever (eternity future)" (Psalm 119:160); "The grass withereth, the flower fadeth: but the word of our God shall stand for ever" (Isaiah 40:8). ". . . the word of God is not bound" (II Timothy 2:9); ". . . for Thou hast magnified Thy Word above all Thy Name" (Psalm 138:2). Amen.

V

THE GENESIS FLOOD — ITS NATURE AND SIGNIFICANCE[1]

PART I

The great Flood of Genesis plays a uniquely important role in the continuing conflict between the Bible and naturalistic science, a fact far too seldom realized even by evangelical Christians. For, if a worldwide Flood actually destroyed all men and land animals except those preserved in a special ark constructed by Noah, and increased to such an extent that for a number of months "all the high mountains that were under the whole heaven were covered" (Genesis 7:19), as the Bible plainly declares, then the very foundation of the materialistic, evolutionary framework of modern philosophic scientism is immediately undermined.

To Charles Lyell (1797-1875), "the high priest of uniformitarianism," the very thought of catastrophism in nature was abhorrent. He insisted that the strata of the earth were laid down over inconceivably vast periods of time by extremely gradual processes of erosion and sedimentation, and that "the present is the key to the past." Charles Darwin found Lyellian uniformitarianism to be the perfect environment for his theory of evolution by natural selection and the survival of the fittest, for he recognized that a tremendous span of time was of supreme importance in theorizing that the only real "proof" that organic evolution is a historical fact is found in the story of the fossils in the sedimentary rock strata of the earth, which have been interpreted in strict conformity to the uniformitarian principle.

The purpose of Part I of this chapter is to discover what the Scriptures have to say concerning these opposing concepts of uniformitarianism and catastrophism, as brought to focus in the question of the Flood. In Part II, the presuppositions of uniformitarian geology and organic evolution will be examined in the light of the Biblical evidence.

The Testimony of the Apostle Peter

The Apostle Peter clearly foresaw the future dominance and danger of naturalistic uniformitarianism, and uttered an emphatic

---

[1]Co-author, John C. Whitcomb, Jr. This article originally appeared in *Bibliotheca Sacra*, Part I in April, 1960 and Part II in July, 1960.

warning against it. In II Peter 3:3-7 we read: ". . . Knowing this
first, that in the last days mockers shall come with mockery, walking after their own lusts, and saying, Where is the promise of His
coming? for, from the day that the fathers fell asleep, all things
continue as they were from the beginning of the Creation. For this
they willingly forget, that there were heavens from of old, and an
earth compacted out of the water and amidst water, by the
word of God, by which the world that then was, being overflowed
with water, perished; but the heavens that now are, and the
earth, by the same word have been stored up for fire, being reserved against the day of judgment and destruction of ungodly
men" (ASV).

In this passage of Scripture, Peter speaks of a day, yet future
from his standpoint, when men would no longer think seriously of
Christ's second coming as a cataclysmic, universal intervention by
God into the course of world affairs. And the reason for this
skeptical attitude would be none other than a blind adherence to
the doctrine of total uniformitarianism — a doctrine which maintains that natural laws and processes have never yet been in-
terrupted so as to bring about a total destruction of human society
and civilization through a supernatural act of God. And since
this has never been the case in past history, there should be no
cause to fear that it will ever occur in the future.

In answering these skeptics of the end-time, Peter points to two
events of the past which cannot be explained on the basis of
naturalistic uniformitarianism. The first of these events is the
creation of the world: "there were heavens from of old, and an
earth . . . by the word of God"; and the second event is the Flood:
"the world (kosmos) that then was, being overflowed with water,
perished (apoleto)."

But it is the second of these two events, the Flood, which serves
as the basis of Peter's comparison with the second coming and
the final destruction of the world. For even as "the world that
then was" perished by water, so "the heavens that now are, and
the earth," protected as they are, by God's eternal promise,
from another aqueous cataclysm (Genesis 9:8-19), have, nevertheless, been stored up for fire, "being reserved against the day of
judgment and destruction of ungodly men."

Let us now consider the implications of this passage with respect
to the geographical extent of the Flood. In speaking of the events
of the second and third days of creation, Peter used the terms
"heavens from of old, and an earth" in a sense that is obviously
universal. By the same token, no one can deny that Peter also
uses the terms "heavens that now are, and the earth" in the strictly
universal sense. Otherwise, Peter would be speaking of the creation
and final destruction of only a part of the earth.

Now it is important to note that one single event which Peter sets forth as having brought about a transformation — not of the earth only, but also of the very heavens — is the Flood. It was the Flood that constituted the line of demarcation between "the heavens from of old" and "the heavens that now are" in the thinking of the Apostle Peter. It was the Flood that utilized the vast oceans of water out of which and amidst which the ancient earth was "compacted," unto the utter destruction of the cosmos "that then was." It was the Flood to which Peter appealed as his final and incontrovertible answer to those who chose to remain in willful ignorance of the fact that God had at one time in the past demonstrated His holy wrath and omnipotence by subjecting "all things" to an overwhelming, cosmic catastrophe that was on an absolute par with the final day of judgment, in which God will yet consume the earth with fire and will cause the very elements to dissolve with fervent heat.

Now if the Noahic Deluge had been merely a local river flood in Mesopotamia, as so many contemporary scholars insist (including many evangelicals who feel it mandatory to yield to all scientific theories), it is difficult to see how Peter's appeal to the Flood would have any value as a contradiction to the doctrine of naturalistic uniformitarianism, which assumes that "all things" have never yet been upset by a universal catastrophe. Nor is it easy to excuse Peter of gross inaccuracy when he depicts the Flood in such cosmic terms and in such an absolutely universal context, if the Flood was only a local inundation after all.

Thus, the third chapter of Second Peter provides powerful New Testament support for the doctrine of a geographically universal and geologically significant Flood in the early days of human history. Anything less than a catastrophe of such worldwide proportions would void the entire force of Peter's argument, and would give much encouragement to the skeptics whom he so solemnly warned.

The Depth of the Flood

The clearest Biblical evidence concerning the depth of the Flood is found in Genesis 7:19, 20; "And the waters prevailed exceedingly upon the earth; and all the high mountains that were under the whole heaven were covered. Fifteen cubits upward did the water prevail; and the mountains were covered." The tremendous scientific implications of these words are obvious. If only one (instead of all) of the high mountains of even the Ararat region had been covered with water, the Flood would have been absolutely universal, for water must seek its own level — and must do so quickly. The phrase "fifteen cubits and upward did the water prevail" is

explained by Genesis 6:15, where we are told that the height of
the Ark was thirty cubits. Most commentators agree that in the
light of this verse, the "fifteen cubits" of 7:20 must refer to the
draft of the Ark. In other words, the Ark sank into the water to a
depth of fifteen cubits (just one half of its height) when fully
laden. Such information adds further strength to this argument for
a universal Flood, because it tells us that the Flood waters "prevailed" over the tops of the highest mountains to a depth of at
least fifteen cubits. If the Flood had not covered the mountains by
at least such a depth, the Ark could not have floated over them
during the five months in which the waters "prevailed" upon the
earth.

The Duration of the Flood

A careful study of the Biblical data reveals the fact that the
Flood lasted for 371 days, or a little more than a year. Such a
duration of time is entirely in keeping with the concept of a universal Flood, but cannot be reconciled with the theory of uniformity
Not only do the Scriptures inform us that the waters prevailed for
five months (150 days), but also that an additional seven months
were required for the waters to subside sufficiently for Noah to
disembark in the mountains of Ararat.

Nor were the Flood waters calm and peaceful during these 150
days of "prevailing," for we read in Genesis 7:11 that "on the same
day were all the fountains of the great deep broken up." The
phrase "great deep" (tehom rabbah) refers to the oceanic depths
(cf. Genesis 1:2 — "deep") and also to subterranean waters. Presumably, then, the ocean floors were cleaved open and uplifted
sufficiently to pour waters over the continents, in conjunction with
those waters which were "above the firmament (i.e., expanse)"
that poured down through "the windows of heaven" (cf. Genesis 1:6-8).

Now these geological phenomena were not confined to a single
day. In fact, the Scriptures reveal that this breaking up of "the
fountains of the great deep" continued for a period of five months;
for it was not until after an elapse of 150 days that "the fountains
of the deep . . . were stopped" (8:2). There can be no question
that these great oceanic upheavals, the driving rains, and the resulting raging flood waters, not only girdled the earth but also had
profound effects on the geologic structure of the earth's crust. The
theory of uniformity, which willfully ignores these geologic effects
of the Flood, thus stands condemned by Scripture as built upon a
false foundation.

According to Genesis 6:15, Noah was commanded to make "the
length of the ark three hundred cubits, the breadth of it fifty

cubits, and the height of it thirty cubits." While it is certainly possible that the cubit of Genesis 6 was longer than the ordinary cubit used by the Hebrews, we shall base our calculations on the 18-inch cubit. "According to this standard," wrote Dr. Alexander Heidel of the Oriental Institute of the University of Chicago, "the Ark was 450 feet long, 75 feet wide, and 45 feet high, and had a displacement of approximately 43,300 tons."[2]

Thus, the Ark was a vessel of three decks with a capacity of 1,518,750 cubic feet, a deck area totaling 101,250 square feet, and a displacement of over 43,000 tons, nearly equal to that of the ill-fated Titanic. For Noah to have built an ark of such gigantic proportions for only eight people and a few animals from the Near East is quite fantastic. For those who take Genesis at face value, the very size of the Ark argues powerfully for a universal Flood.

To carry the matter a step further, not only would an ark of such size have been unnecessary for a local inundation, but there would have been no need for an ark at all. The entire Biblical record of the Flood becomes almost ridiculous if it is conceived in terms of a local flood. The whole procedure of constructing a great boat, involving a tremendous amount of work, can hardly be described as anything but utterly foolish and unnecessary. How much more sensible it would have been for God merely to have warned Noah of the coming destruction, so that he could have moved to another region to which the Flood would not reach. The great numbers of animals of all kinds, and certainly the birds, could easily have moved out also, without having to be stored and tended for a year in the Ark. The entire story thus becomes little more than nonsense if it is taken as a mere local flood in Mesopotamia.

To our knowledge, nô saitsfactory explanation has ever been made for the construction of an ark by Noah "to the saving of his house" (Hebrews 11:7), other than on the postulation of a universal Flood. Until such an explanation is forthcoming, it must be conceded that the local-flood theory and uniformitarianism cannot be made to harmonize with Scripture.

The Destruction of Humanity

Our final argument for a universal Flood is founded upon the Biblical testimony to the total destruction of the human race outside of the Ark. In the first place, there are at least four Biblical reasons for the necessity of a total destruction of humanity in the

---

[2]Alexander Heidel: *The Gilgamesh Epic and Old Testament Parallels*, University of Chicago Press, 1949, 2nd ed., p. 236.

days of Noah: (1) since the stated purpose of the Flood was the punishment of a sinful race, such a purpose could not have been accomplished if only a part of humanity had been affected; (2) the fact that the Flood destroyed the rest of mankind is greatly strengthened by repeated statements in Genesis 6-9, I Peter 3:20, and II Peter 2:5, to the effect that only Noah and his family were spared; (3) our Lord Jesus Christ clearly stated that all men were destroyed by the Flood (Luke 17:26-30); and (4) the covenant which God made with Noah after the Flood (Genesis 9:12) becomes meaningless if only a part of the human race has been involved.

In addition to these arguments for the total destruction of humanity, we submit two reasons for believing that the human race could not have been confined to the Mesopotamian Valley at the time of the Flood: (1) the longevity and fecundity of the antediluvians would allow for a very rapid increase in population, and the prevalence of strife and violence would have tended to encourage wide distribution rather than confinement to a single locality; and (2) evidence from paleontology tends to support a very wide distribution of the human race at the dawn of history rather than a localization within the boundaries of Mesopotamia.

It is our conviction that these basic Scriptural teachings should settle once and for all the long-debated question of the geographical extent of the Food. This is not to say, of course, that a universal Flood presents no serious scientific problems to the modern mind. But we do maintain that no problem, be it scientific or philosophical, can be of sufficient magnitude to offset the combined force of these Biblical arguments for a geographically universal Flood in the days of Noah.

The Interpretation of Universal Terms

In concluding our discussion of the Biblical evidence for a universal Deluge, we must consider briefly one objection that is often raised against this doctrine. It is that universal terms, such as *all* and *every*, need not be understood invariably in the strictly literal sense. For example, when we read in Genesis 41:57 that all countries came into Egypt to buy grain, we are not to interpret this as meaning that people from Australia and America came to Egypt for grain. And thus, by the same token, the statement in Genesis 7:19, that all the high mountains that were under the whole heaven were covered, may be interpreted to mean some high mountains under part of the heavens.

But there are at least two major considerations that render this interpretation untenable. In the first place, the whole tenor of the.

Flood account demands that the universal terms be understood in the literal sense. The analogy with Genesis 41:57 breaks down here because the constant repetition of the universal terms throughout the four chapters of Genesis 6-9 shows conclusively that the question of the magnitude and geographical extent of the Flood is not a merely incidental or relative one in the mind of the author, but is rather one of fundamental importance to the entire Flood narrative. In fact, so frequent and varied are such universal terms and so tremendous are the points of comparison ("high mountains" and "whole heaven") that it is impossible to imagine what more could have been said than actually was said to express the concept of a universal Deluge.

Even more important, however, in deciding the significance of the universal terms employed in Genesis 6-9, is the fact that the physical phenomena described in those chapters would be quite inconceivable if the Flood had been confined to one section of the globe. While it would have been entirely possible for a seven-year famine to grip the Near East without affecting Australia and America (cf. Genesis 41:57), it would not have been possible for water to cover even one high mountain in the Near East without inundating Australia and America as well.

Thus, the argument for a limited interpretation of universal terms in Genesis 6-9 fails to do justice to the demands of Biblical exegesis and must therefore be rejected. As well might one contend that the Creation account of Genesis 1 refers to only a part of the earth as to maintain that the Flood was localized. If language means anything at all, and if the Bible is to be acknowledged as the Word of God, then we must adjust our thinking to the astounding fact that a mighty deluge of waters once covered our entire planet for a year, destroying all air-breathing creatures outside of the Ark "wherein few, that is, eight souls, were saved" (I Peter 3:20).

PART II

The unique significance of the great Flood of Genesis to the present generation lies in its conclusive negation of the modern philosophy of evolution. This evolutionary concept very largely conditions the thinking of modern man, not only in scientific disciplines, but also in political, sociological, and even religious studies. In particular, it has supplied the basic intellectual framework for all the influential anti-Christian systems of these latter days. At the recent Darwinian centennial observance at the University of Chicago (November 26, 1959), Sir Julian Huxley, one of the world's most prominent evolutionary biologists, said: "In the evolutionary pattern of thought there is no longer need or room for the supernatural. The earth was not created; it evolved. So did all the animals and plants that inhabit it, including our human selves, mind and soul, as well as brain and body. So did religion."[3]

Sir Julian has been broadcasting these opinions for over forty years, and it is significant that evidently none of the two thousand leading scientists who had gathered from all over the world at the Chicago convocation raised any public objection to his assertions. The general commitment of the world intellectual community to this type of philosophy is well known to all who are at all conversant with modern scientific literature.

But far too few people realize what a fragile foundation supports the tremendous superstructure of evolutionary speculation. Most of the stock textbook arguments for evolution — the evidence from comparative anatomy, from gene mutations, from embryological resemblances, etc., are entirely circumstantial and can be much better explained in terms of divine creation. The only direct evidence for evolution is that from paleontology, the study of the fossil record. The Yale geologist, Carl Dunbar, recognizes this when he says: "Although the comparative study of living animals and plants may give very convincing circumstantial evidence, fossils provide the only historical documentary evidence that life has evolved from simpler to more complex forms."[4] Similarly, the geneticist Goldschmidt, after admitting the inconclusiveness of the other evidence for evolution, says:

Fortunately, there is a science which is able to observe the progress of evolution through the history of our earth. Geology traces the rocky strata of our earth, deposited one upon another in the past biological epochs through hundreds of millions of years, and finds out their order and timing and reveals organisms which lived in all these periods. Paleontology, which studies the fossil remains, is thus enabled to present organic evolution as a visible fact.[5]

Thus the great billion-year-long drama of evolution is supposedly engraved in the very rocks of the earth as a fact of history, plainly contradicting the divinely inspired account of the method and the order of creation as recorded in the Holy Scriptures!

But, "let God be held true, but every man a liar" (Romans 3:4). The Christian is surely entitled, in view of his assurance of the full divine reliability and perspicuity of Scripture, to raise a few questions about the real significance of these fossils. Just

---

[3]Associated Press Dispatch, November 27, 1959.

[4]Carl O. Dunbar: *Historical Geology* (2nd ed., New York, Wiley, 1960), p. 47.

[5]R. Goldschmidt: "An Introduction to a Popularized Symposium on Evolution," *Scientific Monthly*, 77:184, October, 1953.

how and when were the various rocks formed, and how do we know? How are different rocks dated relative to each other? Do superposed strata really exhibit a continuous gradation of fossil forms tracing the gradual evolution of all things? Perhaps it is presumptuous to ask such questions of those who are authorities in these matters (as they are always quick to remind any outsider who does), but the profound importance of the issue nevertheless demands that we do so.

The method of dating sedimentary rocks and their contained fossils is clarified by the following statement, from a highly qualified European geologist:

> The only chronometric scale applicable in geologic history for the stratigraphic classification of rocks and for dating geological events exactly is furnished by the fossils. Owing to the irreversibility of evolution, they offer an unambiguous time-scale for relative age determinations and for worldwide correlation of rocks.[6]

In other words, rocks are dated purely and simply by means of the fossils they contain. The guiding principle in this method of dating is the assumed irreversibility of evolution, so that the state of evolution attained by the creatures entombed in the strata is adequate indication of the "exact" age of the rocks. This is confirmed by two prominent American geologists: "The geologist utilizes knowledge of organic evolution as preserved in the fossil record, to identify and correlate the lithic records of ancient time."[7]

Thus, organic evolution is assumed as a known fact by paleontologists in building up their geologic time scale, rocks containing simpler fossils being dated as old and those containing more complex fossils being called young. Superposition, lithologic composition and other factors are of secondary importance in assigning a date to a given rock stratum. Nowhere in the world is there found a continuous vertical sequence of rocks comprising even a fair segment of the supposed 100-mile thick geologic column. The latter has been built up by hypothetical superposition of rocks from all over the world, arranged on the basis of the assumed principle of organic evolution. And the remarkable thing is that the geologic column thus erected is offered as the one *factual* proof that evolution is true! This would seem to be a remarkable example of circular reasoning. The British geologist, Rastall, admits as much, when he says:

> It cannot be denied that from a strictly philosophical standpoint geologists are here arguing in a circle. The succession of organisms has been determined by a study of their remains embedded in the

---

[6]O. H. Schindewolf, "Comments on Some Stratigraphic Terms," *American Journal of Science*, 255:394, June, 1957.

[7]O. D. von Engeln and K. E. Caster, *Geology*, (New York, McGraw-Hill 1952), p. 423.

rocks and the relative ages of the rocks are determined by the remains of organisms that they contain.[8]

But geologists maintain that the system has proved its validity by the fact that it has worked so well, serving now for over a hundred years as the chief basis of geologic dating and correlation. And there can be no question that the fossils *have* served satisfactorily in this capacity and they *do* exhibit, in general, a gradation from simple to complex. The geologists and paleontologists who utilize this geologic time scale are intelligent and honest men, and we do not impugn their motives or abilities when we question the evolutionary and uniformitarian interpretations that have been placed on their data.

But even if we accept the geologic time scale as valid, we find therein little evidence of real evolution. The gaps that exist between biologic families in the present world, and even to a considerable extent those that exist between genera and species, are essentially duplicated in the fossil record. The paleontologist Simpson has recognized this:

> In spite of these examples, it remains true, as every paleontologist knows, that *most* new species, genera, and families, and that nearly all categories above the level of families, appear in the record suddenly, and are not led up to by known, gradual, completely continuous transitional sequences.[9]

Simpson was speaking mainly of fossil animals. The paleobotanist Arnold finds the same situation true with respect to plant evolution:

> It has long been hoped that extinct plants will ultimately reveal some of the stages through which existing groups have passed during the course of their development, but it must be freely admitted that this aspiration has been fulfilled to a very slight extent, even though paleobotanical research has been in progress for more than one hundred years. As yet we have not been able to trace the phylogenetic history of a single group of modern plants from its beginning to the present.[10]

Thus do innumerable gaps exist in the assumed fossil record of evolution, even though evolution has been the main criterion for building up the record.

As might be expected in view of the arbitrary manner in which the geologic column has been built up, numerous anomalies and contradictions are evident in it. Laymen generally have the impression that there is an essentially uniform and complete vertical

---

[8]R. H. Rastall: "Geology," *Encyclopedia Britannica*, 1956, X, 168.

[9]George Gaylord Simpson: *The Major Features of Evolution*, (New York, Columbia University Press, 1953), p. 360.

[10]C. A. Arnold: *An Introduction to Paleobotany*, (McGraw-Hill, 1947), p. 7.

column of geologic formations around the earth, with the oldest at the bottom and the youngest at the top. Geologists, of course, realize that this is not the case. E. M. Spieker, Professor of Geology at Ohio State University, says: "Further, how many geologists have pondered the fact that lying on the crystalline basement are found from place to place not merely Cambrian, but rocks of all ages?"[11]

Not only are the lowest formations likely to be composed of rocks of any age from the oldest to the youngest, but the vertical order of formations at any one site may consist of any combination of age units, with rocks of any age lying on top of those of any other age.

The most anomalous situation, of course, is when rocks dated as old are found lying directly over those dated as young. And this is a very common phenomenon in geology.[12] Such anomalous sequences are rationalized in terms of great earth movements that somehow thrust old strata up and over those that were younger, with subsequent erosion removing the younger strata still resting on top of the "thrust block." And the existence of these remarkable inversions is proved by the fossils.

> Of course, there are many places where the succession has been locally inverted by folding or interrupted by faulting, but such exceptions will betray themselves in the evidences of disturbance and in the unnatural succession of the fossils.[13]

Evidences of disturbance are sometimes present (as they also frequently are in regions where the fossils appear in their "proper" evolutionary order) and sometimes absent, but the real basis of the interpretation is the inverted sequence of the fossils. Geophysicists have difficulty in explaining such events:

> Since their earliest recognition, the existence of large overthrusts has presented a mechanical paradox that has never been satisfactorily resolved. . . . Consequently, for the conditions assumed, the pushing of a thrust block, whose length is of the order of 30 kilometers or more, along a horizontal surface, appears to be a mechanical impossibility.[14]

---

[11]E. M. Spieker: "Mountain-Building Chronology and Nature of Geologic Time-Scale," *Bulletin, American Association of Petroleum Geologists,* 40:1805, August, 1956.

[12]M. King Hubbert and W. W. Rubey give an extensive listing of areas of this type, "Role of Fluid Pressure in the Mechanics of Overthrust Faulting," *Bulletin, Geological Society of America,* 70:119-22, February, 1959.

[13]Charles Schuchert and C. O. Dunbar, *Outlines of Historical Geology,* (Wiley, 1943), p. 5.

[14]Hubbert and Rubey, *op. cit.,* pp. 122, 126. The hypothesis of these authors is that the thrust blocks were "floated" into place by means of huge internal fluid pressures.

And the only need for contriving explanations for "mechanical impossibilities" is to preserve the postulated evolutionary sequences in the fossiliferous rocks. One begins to sense that the fossil record, supposedly the best documentation of the fact of organic evolution, in actuality is a record of some altogether different fact of history.

From the perspective of Biblical revelation, we would say that the root of the difficulty is really in the basic scientific doctrine of "uniformitarianism." This is the doctrine that all past changes in the earth and its components must be explained in terms of principles and processes that are still operative today — "the present is the key to the past." The phenomena of erosion, sedimentation, radioactivity, diastrophism, etc., — all operating in essentially the same fashion and at the same rates as at the present — are supposed to be able to explain the origin and formation of all the earth's geologic deposits and indeed finally the origin and development of the universe itself.

> This is the great underlying principle of modern geology and is known as the principle of uniformitarianism. . . . Without the principle of uniformitarianism there could hardly be a science of geology that was more than pure description.[15]

The concept of uniformity in present processes is, of course, perfectly valid and is absolutely basic to the scientific method. But when present processes are projected backward (or forward) and are presumed to be essentially eternal in duration and infinite in application, then conflict with Biblical revelation is inevitable. According to the inspired account given in Genesis 1, the creation of the world and everything in it was completed within the six-day period there described. Regardless of whether the creative days are to be interpreted literally or not, there can be no question that the Creation was completed (and therefore not still continuing), and this fact was memorialized by the institution of the Sabbath. This is strongly emphasized in the Genesis record: "Thus the heavens and the earth were finished, and all the host of them. And on the seventh day God ended his work which he had made, and he rested on the seventh day from all his work which he had made. And God blessed the seventh day, and sanctified it: because that in it he had rested from all his work which he had made. And God blessed the seventh day, and sanctified it: because that in it he had rested from all his work which God created and made" (Genesis 2:1-3; cf. Exodus 20:8-11; Hebrews 4:3, 4, 10).

It is therefore quite certain that the present processes of nature are *not* creative processes, because the whole Creation was com-

---

[15]W. D. Thornbury, *Principles of Geomorphology*, (Wiley, 1954), pp. 16, 17.

pleted at that time. This, of course, is confirmed by the great scientific principle of mass and energy conservation, the first law of thermodynamics, the most basic and best established of all scientific laws. There is no *creation* of matter or energy now taking place in the universe, so far as scientific measurements are concerned. Consequently, the principle of uniformity, which assumes that the processes by which the universe and the earth were organized into their present forms are the same processes by which they are now *maintained*, runs directly counter to the explicit statement of Scripture and to basic scientific law.

Furthermore, the Edenic Curse, pronounced not only on man but also on the physical dominion of man, implies that there is now in the world a pervasive principle of natural deterioration and disorganization. This principle manifests itself in the natural order in what is now known as the second law of thermodynamics, the law that "entropy" (a mathematical measure of the state of disorder of any system) must continuously increase as long as the system receives no new organizing energy from outside itself. The physicist Lindsay puts it thus:

> On this interpretation, the meaning of the second law of thermodynamics, the law of increasing entropy, is now clear. In any naturally occurring process, the tendency is for all systems to proceed from order to disorder. From this point of view, the trend from order to disorder with production of entropy is inexorable. The second law always wins in the end.[16]

The two laws of thermodynamics are as nearly universal in application as any laws yet known. The Harvard physicist, Bridgman, says concerning them:

> The two laws of thermodynamics are, I suppose, accepted by physicists as perhaps the most secure generalizations from experience we have. The physicist does not hesitate to apply the two laws to any concrete physical situation in the confidence that nature will not let him down.[17]

And these two laws strongly confirm the revealed fact of a completed Creation of all things, originally pronounced "very good" by its Creator, but since fallen into a state of "bondage to decay" (Romans 8:21, ASV). Instead of uniformity of all things since the "beginning of Creation" (II Peter 3:4), there exists a profound discontinuity in the history of all present natural processes at the time of the completion of Creation.

But the question still remains as to the true significance of the geologic formations, in particular those containing the fossilized

---

[16]R. B. Lindsay: "Entropy Consumption and Values in Physical Science," *American Scientist*, 47:382, September, 1959.

[17]P. W. Bridgman: "Reflections on Thermodynamics," *American Scientist*, 5:41:549, October, 1953.

remains of creatures which once lived on the earth. If they do not record the history of earth's evolution into its present state, just what do they record?

The Bible clearly teaches that suffering and death entered the world as a result of God's Curse thereon following man's sin (Genesis 2:17; 3:17-19; Romans 5:12; 8:18-22; I Corinthians 15:21; etc.). The fossil record, which includes both men and animals, speaks as eloquently of death in earlier times as the daily obituary columns do in modern times. Thus, it is obvious that the geologic column does not record the history of creation, since the processes by which the strata were laid down were not creative processes at all, but rather reveals graphically the fact of suffering and death in an earth now groaning and travailing in pain, under bondage to the principle of decay and corruption. Therefore, they must have been deposited since the beginning of human history, and this can only mean that they were laid down largely under sudden and catastrophic conditions rather than under gradual and uniformist conditions.

These considerations lead us inexorably back to the great Flood of Genesis as the agency necessarily responsible for the formation of many, perhaps most, of the fossil-bearing rocks of the earth's crust. This tremendous cataclysm, accompanied as it was by torrential global downpours lasting for forty days and forty nights, by the breaking-up of all the fountains of the great deep for one hundred and fifty days, by waters rolling over the tops of the highest mountains for still seventy-four more days, and by many other uniquely intense hydrologic and geophysical phenomena, marked the greatest divine judgment on sin and therefore the greatest visitation of death on this earth since the world began.

We have already, in Part I of this study, shown that Scripture very plainly and emphatically teaches that the Flood was worldwide in extent, both anthropologically and geographically. The local-flood concept may placate evolutionists to some extent, but it denies the Word of God, and this is a poor exchange. And if the Flood was universal, and if the known principles of hydrology and sedimentation have any meaning, an unprecedented hydrodynamic convulsion of this character must have completely broken up the crustal rocks and soils of the antediluvian earth. Furthermore, it must have finally redeposited them in great beds of sedimentary strata which soon hardened into rock, with millions of animate creatures of all kinds (especially those inhabiting the seas and lowlands) entombed within them.

Thus the very rocks of the earth must bear witness to the fact of God's judgment on sin, as well as to the truth of His Word. Further, they serve to emphasize the frequent Biblical warning of a still greater judgment by fire yet to come. With reference to the scientific study of earth history, the Flood constitutes such a great gap in the continuity of even those natural processes, prevailing since the end of the Creation period, that it renders invalid any method of geological chronology based on the assumption of continuity.

We realize that this conclusion leads one into numerous geological problems of great magnitude. There are many types of geologic formations and deposits which seem superficially to require great lengths of time for their origin and development. However, these appearances are only superficial, because the phenomena have been viewed through evolutionary and uniformitarian spectacles. We believe it is quite possible (in fact, it must be so) to harmonize all the real geologic data with a full acceptance of the Biblical record of earth history. Although long and intense study would be required on the part of many evangelical scientists to accomplish such a task, its potential value, both for true science and for Biblical Christianity, would abundantly warrant the dedication of many Christian scholars to this purpose.

Present trends, even in the last strongholds of evangelical Christianity, indicate a real danger that modern intellectual uniformitarianism and evolutionism, with all the ills that follow in their train, may soon dilute and dissipate the last vestiges of truly Biblical faith on the earth. But an awakened recognition of the historical reality of the Genesis Flood, in its true nature and significance, could serve a mighty evangelistic and purifying purpose in the world in these last days.

VI

A Review of

"EVOLUTION AND CHRISTIAN THOUGHT TODAY"[1]

This volume[2] has been prepared under the sponsorship of the American Scientific Affiliation, a group of some eight hundred evangelical scientists committed to Biblical Christianity. Written by thirteen members of the Affiliation and edited by its former president, Russell A. Mixter, who is Professor of Zoology at Wheaton College, the book has been issued in connection with the hundredth anniversary of Charles Darwin's *Origin of Species* and is an attempt to evaluate the theory of evolution from the Christian viewpoint.

Such a work, if satisfactory, would be timely and is urgently needed. The evolutionary philosophy now dominates nearly every sphere of learning and science and is basic in the thinking of the world's intellectual and political leaders. Its conflict with the Biblical revelation of Creation and the Fall is neither peripheral nor superficial, and a book which would bring it into proper Biblical and scientific perspective would render an invaluable service.

But this book, in the judgment of this reviewer, does not meet this need. In their desire to establish a reputation of intellectual respectability for evangelical Christians, the authors have given us essentially a polemic for evolution, apparently with the primary purpose of "educating" their less-informed and more conservative brethren! It is feared that the result will be an acceleration of the already widespread defection of neo-evangelicals to evolutionism and its associated ills.

The authors attempt to evaluate current thought in each of several disciplines concerned with evolution, viewing it in light of the Bible account of origins. Each author writes as a theist, of course, and insists that God is the originator and sustainer of such evolutionary processes as may be operative in nature. Some of the writers retain the view, generally accepted among creationists, that evolution has occurred only within the original-created Genesis "kinds" of organisms, but they do not commit themselves as to the particular limits implied by this term. Others in the

---

[1]This review appeared in *Torch and Trumpet*, December, 1960.

[2]*Evolution and Christian Thought Today* (Grand Rapids, Wm. B. Eerdmans Publishing Company, 1959, 224 pp.)

Symposium appear willing to accept the evolutionary origin of all things, even life itself!

At the same time, several lines of evidence against evolution are very capably presented by at least some of the writers. But then the significance of these evidences is minimized or even ignored.

In Chapter One, Thomas D. S. Key, a high school biology teacher, reviews the influence of Darwin on biology and theology. He lists a number of theories by which various writers have attempted to reconcile Scripture with evolutionary theory, but comes to no particular conclusion himself.

Dr. George Schweitzer, Associate Professor of Chemistry at the University of Tennessee, and a popular lecturer on science and religion, writes on the various theories of the origin of the earth and the universe. Although he admits that each of these theories encounters serious difficulties, he favors Gamow's theory, which postulates the evolutionary development of the universe from a state of extremely high density, beginning some five billion years ago.

Most theistic evolutionists have, in the past, at least accepted the special creation of life itself. So it is rather amazing to find the authors of Chapter Three (Dr. Walter Hearn, Assistant Professor of Chemistry at Iowa State and Dr. Richard Hendry, Associate Professor of Chemistry at Westminster College, New Wilmington, Pennsylvania) now arguing even for a naturalistic origin of living matter from the non-living! They do not, of course, offer any real proof of such a biochemical origin of life. In essence they tell us that perhaps it might have been so, and therefore we ought to accept it!

The chapter on genetics is written by Dr. D. S. Robertson, Assistant Professor of Genetics at Iowa State, and John Sinclair, a student at U.C.L.A. Although these writers do not definitely commit themselves to total evolution, they stress the importance of mutations and natural selection in the evolutionary process. And in typical evolutionist fashion, the highly significant fact that practically all mutations are either neutral or harmful in the struggle for existence is first admitted and then dismissed.

In Chapter Five, Dr. Irving Knobloch, Professor of Natural Science at Michigan State, cites numerous instances of biologic change through the process of hybridization. He recognizes, however, that this process must be within definite limits and affirms his belief in the special creation of the original "kinds" of Genesis. Dr. Wilbur Bullock, Associate Professor of Zoology at the University of New Hampshire, takes a similar position, writing on the evidence from taxonomy. Bullock devotes most of his efforts, however, to demolishing the straw man of absolute fixity of species, which no informed creationist has advocated for many years.

Dr. V. E. Anderson, Professor of Biology at Bethel College, discusses the phenomena of geographical distribution as an evidence for evolution. His position on the creation of original kinds, with subsequent variation within the kinds, is essentially the same as that of Knobloch and Bullock. Anderson ignores the implications of the Noahic Flood, which is necessarily of profound importance in any Biblically-oriented consideration of animal migrations and distribution.

The most important "evidence" for evolution, that from paleontology (the study of fossils) is discussed by Cordelia Erdman Barber, now a housewife but formerly a geology instructor at Wheaton College. Mrs. Barber accepts the fossil sequences as giving an actual documentary record of the history of life on the earth. In view of the limited and circumstantial nature of all the other supposed evidences for evolution, this paleontological evidence has long been regarded by evolutionists as the one real proof of evolution. Mrs. Barber recognizes, however, the existence of serious evolutionary gaps in the fossil record, of basically the same magnitude and kind as those noted in the data from genetics, taxonomy, and other fields. The possible significance of the great Flood in the formation of any of the fossiliferous strata is highhandedly dismissed as unworthy of discussion.

Dr. J. Frank Cassel, Chairman of the Zoology Department at North Dakota State Agricultural College, discusses the anatomical, embryological and physiological resemblances between different groups of animals. He recognizes that these evidences are entirely circumstantial and can well be cited as evidences for a common Designer; he is nevertheless quite willing to accept them as of evolutionary origin.

The important problem of the origin of man is dealt with by J. O. Buswell, III, who is Assistant Professor of Anthropology at Wheaton College. Although Buswell believes in a real Adam, as a special creation of God, he accepts the modern anthropological chronologies of early man, which means that Adam must be dated as at least several hundred thousand years old! He dismisses any problems of Biblical exegesis which this view entails as negligible.

The concluding chapter, which summarizes the book and relates the whole to Christian theology, is by Dr. Carl Henry, editor of the periodical *Christianity Today*. Henry gives an excellent summary and analysis of the present status of evolution in modern thought. He incisively and with full documentation points up the paradox of the universal acceptance of evolution despite the basic deficiencies in its evidential basis. Like several of the other authors, he still favors belief in the special creation of life, of the major forms of organisms, and of man. One gathers, however, that these beliefs could easily be forfeited if the scientific evidence should become strong enough to warrant it.

The book has many commendable features and contains many useful data in conveniently available form. And of course the degree of accommodation of the Christian position to that of the evolutionist is less for some of the authors than for others.

Nevertheless, all of the authors apparently agree on certain very important concessions to the evolutionary system. For example, the geologic ages are accepted in their entirety, implying an age for the earth of some five billion years, an age for life on the earth of perhaps a billion years, and an age for man himself of at least several hundred thousand years! In effect, this position repudiates any genuine historical validity of the Genesis account of creation, reducing it to the level of a poem or allegory. It stretches the chronological framework of Genesis 5 and 11 beyond all reason and ignores the testimony concerning the highly developed civilization of the immediate descendants of Adam and later of Noah.

This position rejects God's statement (in Genesis 2:1-3 and elsewhere) to the effect that the processes of creation, whatever they may have been, were completely terminated after the six days of creation. It also ignores the fact of the Fall and its associated Curse on the whole Creation (Romans 8:20-22). The Biblical testimony of a completed Creation, not continuing in the present, is scientifically supported by the first law of thermodynamics, the law of energy conservation, which states that there is no creation of energy (and this includes matter also) taking place in the universe at the present. Its testimony of present decay and deterioration in nature, resulting from the Fall, is supported scientifically by the second law of thermodynamics, which states that all natural processes tend to go in the direction of increasing disorganization and decreasing complexity, unless acted upon by external sources of energy and information. And these two laws of thermodynamics are without doubt the most firmly established of all known physical laws!

Thus, the Creation was not accomplished by means of the natural processes prevailing at the present time, those processes with which this Symposium deals — such as mutation, natural selection, hybridization, erosion, radio-activity, etc. These processes must all operate within the framework of the two laws of thermodynamics, and therefore could not have been in operation in their present form in the period of the Creation. It is therefore quite impossible to deduce the history of the Creation from the study of these present processes.

Furthermore, the authors have quite ignored the Biblical witness of a universal, earth-shaking Flood in the days of Noah. The record of the Flood, if true, clearly implies tremendous geologic upheavals and profound disturbances in the continuity of even those natural processes in effect in the present cosmos. The dogma of geological uniformitarianism is automatically discredited if a Deluge such as the Bible describes has actually occurred on the earth since the Creation, and this uniformitarian assumption is quite basic to the evolutionary interpretation of the fossil record, which in turn is regarded by evolutionists as the one real proof that their theory is true. To reject, and — still worse — to ignore, the implications of the Deluge in a work which purports to evaluate evolution from the Biblical perspective, is clearly indicative of a very low esteem for Scriptural integrity and perspicuity.

For these and other reasons, this reviewer cannot recommend this book, at least for the purpose for which it was intended. It will undoubtedly prove to be a very influential book, however, and this fact accounts for the rather extensive analysis devoted to it here.

VII

WATER AND THE WORD[1]

"For the first heaven and the first earth were passed away; and there was no more sea" (Revelation 21:1). Perhaps the strangest and most remarkable aspect of the new earth which God will create, after the millennium and the judgment of the dead at the great white throne is the absence of the sea. In the present earth the great oceanic reservoirs of water constitute its predominant geographical feature. Covering over seventy per cent of the earth's surface, the sea is God's great storehouse of water, the amazing substance which uniquely equips our planet earth to be the abode of man.

There are many, many ways in which water is indispensable for life on the earth. Water, for example, is itself the primary component of all living substance. Over two thirds of the human body is water. "The life of the flesh is in the blood" (Leviticus 17:11), and the blood serum is made up of about ninety-two per cent water. All nutrition and digestion processes are carried out by means of a water medium. The growth of plant life, the basic source of food for animal life, requires water, together with light, as prerequisites. In fact, practically all important chemical and biological processes involve water in one way or another.

As far as is known definitely, the earth is the only place in the entire universe where water exists in sufficient quantity to support life. Certainly no known planet contains anything comparable to our present oceans of liquid water, upon which depends the marvelous hydrologic cycle, the physical mechanism by which water is being continuously conveyed from the oceans through the air to meet the water needs of all parts of the earth.

And yet, despite its basic and profound importance on the present earth, the Bible says that one day there will be "no more sea." There will be a new earth and a new atmosphere (heavens), but no sea.

But why? Before we can discern an answer to this question, we need to consider in some detail the history and purpose of the sea and the waters of the earth.

---

[1]This article is reprinted by permission from the July, 1961 issue of *Bibliotheca Sacra*.

The Primeval Ocean

"And darkness was upon the face of the deep" (Genesis 1:2). In the new earth, there will be no sea; on the primeval earth there was a universal sea! In like manner, a global darkness enveloped the earth at first but, on the new earth, "there shall be no night there" (Revelation 21:25).

On the first day of creation, God began to dispel the darkness by commanding light to shine out of the darkness, dividing the light from the darkness, and day from night. In exactly parallel fashion, on the third day, God began to dispel the universal sea by commanding the dry land to appear, dividing the seas from the land, which was prepared as the abode of man.

But between these two activities of division or separation, there was, on the second day, a division of the waters themselves into two great reservoirs, one above the firmament (i.e., the expanse, corresponding probably to our present troposphere) and the other below the firmament. The similarity of terms describing these three acts of division, together with the fact that the first of the three caused a division of the whole day into two approximately equal segments of day and night, perhaps would suggest that each of the other two divisions resulted in two approximately equal segments. If this is a reasonable inference, then the reservoir of waters above the heavens was approximately equal to that left in the seas, and the earth's primeval lands occupied about half its surface.

These were all mighty acts of creation, and we must simply confess that we do not and cannot know what means or processes God employed in bringing them about. Since God "rested from all His works" (Genesis 2:3), and since these works included "heaven and earth, the sea, and all that in them is" (Exodus 20:11), at the end of the six days of creation, we can therefore no longer observe or study these processes of creation. Present-day physical and biological processes must be entirely different; their study, no matter how carefully or scientifically prosecuted, can give us no certain information about God's true creative devices at all. The modern scientific premise of uniformity in natural processes simply cannot be legitimately applied to the Creation period.

The remarkable prophetic warning against latter-day scoffers who use the principle of uniformitarianism in exactly this illegitimate fashion (II Peter 3:3-6) is accompanied by an equally remarkable statement concerning the primary importance of water in the methods and results of the Creation. ". . . There were heavens from of old, and an earth compacted out of water and amidst (marginal rendering 'through') water, by the word of God" (II Peter 3:5, ASV). Varying renderings of this verse are found in different translations, and varying interpretations in different commentaries; perhaps the basic reason for so much difficulty with it is a subconscious insistence on interpreting the events of Creation in terms of our modern scientific concepts and processes.

The word "compacted" is the Greek *sunistemi*, essentially meaning "holding together" or "consisting" (note the same word in Colossians 1:17, where it is said that "all things hold together in Him"). The created earth, originally "without form" (Genesis 1:2) thus was "formed" by the Word of God, by the means of water, and now is sustained by the same means. The first lands were undoubtedly molded by the action of water, and life itself was organized to be nourished and held together in and by a water medium. Finally, a portion of the waters was designed to serve as a great protective canopy for the earth, elevated and sustained "above the firmament," also by the Word of God (Genesis 1:7).

In order for these upper waters to be maintained aloft by the gases of the lower atmosphere and also for it to be transparent to the light of the sun, moon, and stars (Genesis 1:14-16), the canopy must have been in the form of a vast blanket of water vapor, extending far out into space, invisible and yet exerting a profound influence on terrestrial climates and living conditions. It would have insured a worldwide warm, mild climate, with only minor seasonal and latitudinal differences. This in turn would have inhibited the great air circulational patterns which characterize the present world, and which constitute the basic cause of our winds, rains, and storms.

There could have been no rain in the form with which we are familiar, and this is exactly the testimony of Scripture (Genesis 2:5-6). But there was a system of rivers and seas (Genesis 1:10; 2:10-14), nourished probably by waters that had been confined under presssure beneath the lands when the lands and waters were "divided" as well as by the low-lying vapors that were daily evaporated and recondensed (Genesis 2:6). As far as the record goes, these rivers, especially that which emerged from a great artesian spring in the Garden of Eden (Genesis 2:10), were the main sources of water for Adam and his descendants.

The vapor canopy also would have served as a highly effective shield against the many powerful and harmful radiations that surround the earth, and which are now only partially filtered by our present atmosphere. Such radiations are now known to be the cause of many physical damages to man's genetic system, tending to cause harmful mutations and general biological deterioration. It is quite possible that the blanket was one major factor contributing to human longevity in those early days.

The Flood of Waters

"Whereby the world that then was, being overflowed with water, perished" (II Peter 3:6). But sin entered into the world, and death by sin, and then followed a long, sad history of deterioration and rebellion against God. Finally, God determined to "bring a flood of waters upon the earth, to destroy all flesh, wherein is the breath of life, from under heaven; and everything that is in the earth shall die" (Genesis 6:17). To accomplish the earth's cleansing and purification, God chose the very element out of which the earth had been "compacted" and by which its very life was sustained. "Whereby," by this same water, the world of the antediluvians was over-flowed, and perished. The great expanse of waters above the firmament was condensed and plunged to the earth, continuing everywhere at fullest intensity for forty days and forty nights (Genesis 7:12). The "great deep," evidently vast storehouses of the waters under the firmament confined in the seas and under pressure beneath the surface rocks of the earth's crust, also issued forth, as "all the fountains of the great deep were broken up" (Genesis 7:11). This latter upheaval must have been followed by the eruption of subterranean magmas, and these by great earthquakes, and these in turn by tremendous tidal waves in the seas. Destruction beyond imagination must have been wrought on the antediluvian earth!

Finally, the waters prevailed upon the earth to such a height that "all the high hills, that were under the whole heaven, were covered," and "the mountains were covered," and "all flesh died that moved upon the earth, both of fowl, and of cattle, and of beast, and of every creeping thing that creepeth upon the earth, and every man" (Genesis 7:19-21). Once again, as in the beginning, there was a universal ocean. The same waters which had sustained the life of the world now became its shroud.

Furthermore, there was again "darkness upon the face of the deep," although not the total darkness that originally was present. When the vast vapor canopy condensed into liquid water and began to fall as rain, it was necessarily converted into a great mass of cloud, of such vast depths that only very small amounts of the sun's light could penetrate. And although the greatest of the rains and upheavals continued only for forty days, they continued in some degree of intensity until "restrained" after 150 days (Genesis 7:24–8:2).

But the darkness was not total, nor was death universal. Noah had "found grace," and God had an Ark of safety. The same waters which brought death to the "world of the ungodly" (II Peter 2:5) were those which bore up the Ark, "wherein few, that is, eight souls were saved by water" (I Peter 3:20). Here at the great Flood, in the most stark and vivid outline, is portrayed the paradox of water, and the spiritual realities which it typifies. Water is both a vehicle of life and a vehicle of death and judgment.

Poured Out

The waters of the Flood were literally poured forth from the windows of Heaven by a wrathful God, destroying the whole world that then was. But this tremendous baptism in water was not only a baptism unto death but also a baptism unto life, delivering those who were in the Ark from the filth and corruption of the antediluvians, which would otherwise have engulfed them.

Consider this remarkable phrase, "poured out" or "shed" (both being translations of the Hebrew *shaphak*). This word is used frequently in Scripture of the "pouring-out" of the indignation and wrath of God (e.g., Psalm 69:24; Isaiah 42:25; Hosea 5:10; etc). On the other hand, it is also used in connection with great poured-out blessing, as when He says: "And it shall come to pass afterward that I will pour out my Spirit upon all flesh" (Joel 2:28).

But it is used *first of all* immediately after the great Flood had been poured out, in connection with the pouring out, not of water, but of *blood!* "Whoso sheddeth man's blood, by man shall his blood be shed: for in the image of God made He man" (Genesis 9:6). The sacredness of human life, and of the blood maintaining that life, is thus emphasized by God, with the basic reason given being the image of God in man. But undoubtedly there is in view here, ultimately, the one who as Son of Man would yet be the "image of the invisible God" (Colossians 1:15), and whose precious blood would one day be "shed" by man.

This is the same word which is used again and again of the blood of the sacrificial offerings, "poured out" at the base of the altar (e.g., Leviticus 4:30; etc.). And this was all symbolic of that "blood of the New Testament, which is shed for many for the remission of sins" (Matthew 26:28).

And finally this is the word used prophetically of His sufferings upon the cross, when He cried: "I am poured out like water, and all my bones are out of joint: my heart is like wax; it is melted in the midst of my bowels" (Psalm 22:14). Notice how strongly John emphasizes the pouring out of both blood and water. "But one of the soldiers with a spear pierced His side, and forthwith came there out blood and water. And he that saw it bare record, and his record is true: and he knoweth that he saith true, that ye might believe" (John 19:34, 35).

The Spirit, and the Water, and the Blood

We can begin to discern, then, not only something of the physical significance of the waters of the earth, but also of the spiritual. Absolutely essential to physical life, in numerous ways, they nevertheless can be the agent of suffering and death. They are most intimately essential to the life of man through his blood, which is not only made up almost wholly of water but which requires the instrumentality of the water taken into the body to convey the necessary nourishment from all his intake of food. The life of the flesh is in the blood, and the blood is constituted in a matrix of water. And when the blood is poured out, even as the waters of the Flood were poured out, death ensues. But when the blood and water were poured out at the base of the cross, when He "poured out His soul unto death" (Isaiah 53:12), there was somehow released a "well of water springing up into everlasting life" (John 4:14).

And the spiritual reality of which this speaks is nothing less than the outpouring of the Holy Spirit, in a glorious baptism into Christ Himself. "For I will pour water upon him that is thirsty, and floods upon the dry ground: I will pour my spirit upon thy seed, and my blessing upon thine offspring" (Isaiah 44:3). "Not by works of righteousness which we have done, but according to His mercy He saved us, by the washing of regeneration, and renewing of the Holy Ghost; which He shed (i.e., 'poured out') on us abundantly through Jesus Christ our Saviour" (Titus 3:5, 6).

Thus do water and the blood and the Holy Spirit all testify of the great fact of death to sin and eternal life in Christ, imparted to us through faith in Him and His atoning death. "This is He that came by water and blood, even Jesus Christ; not by water only, but by water and blood. And it is the Spirit that beareth witness, because the Spirit is truth. And there are three that bear witness in earth, the Spirit, and the water, and the blood; and these three agree in one" (I John 5:6-8).

The Heavens and the Earth Which Are Now

With the precipitation of the vapor canopy, there was no longer the worldwide warm climate that prevented the development of winds and storms. Soon great winds began to blow (Genesis 8:1), generating great waves and currents (Genesis 8:3); perhaps these forces also triggered the tectonic forces which must have been acting when "the waters hasted away (the mountains rose, the valleys sank down) unto the place which Thou hadst founded for them. Thou hast set a bound that they may not pass over; that they turn not again to cover the earth" (Psalm 104:6-9 ASV).

An entirely different climatic mechanism henceforth prevailed. Distinct seasons were inaugurated (Genesis 8:22), and the rainbow was established (Genesis 9:13), neither of which was possible with the antediluvian vapor capony. Furthermore, human life-spans began to decline, probably as a result of the increase in atmospheric radiations and the general austerity of climate and living conditions.

But in spite of the loss of many of the favorable aspects of earlier climatic controls, even the present hydrologic cycle is marvelously effective, and in fact quite indispensable, in maintaining life on the earth. Much scientific study has been devoted to it and, although it is still not understood in many of its details, the broad outlines have been deciphered within the past hundred years or so. And it is significant that the many Biblical references to the various phases of the hydrologic cycle are thoroughly in harmony with the most modern perspectives in this science.

The oceans, of course, are much larger than they were before the Flood, now containing the waters formerly "above the firmament," as well as those released through the "fountains of the great deep." It is these that now constitute the great "storehouses" of water that are essential for the operation of the water cycle (Psalm 33:7). Waters are evaporated from the oceans (Psalm 135:7), carried inland by the winds (Ecclesiastes 1:6), caused to encounter particles of dust and sea salt to serve as nuclei of condensation (Proverbs 8:26), condense into liquid water droplets in the form of clouds (Job 26:8), which in turn under the proper conditions coalesce and fall as rain (Job 36:27, 28), providing water for maintenance of life on the earth (Isaiah 55:10), and finally return by the rivers to the oceans from which they came (Ecclesiastes 1:7).

The waters in the present atmosphere are of much smaller volume than those above the antediluvian "firmament," amounting to an equivalent depth of less than two inches distributed uniformly over the earth, underscoring the fact that there could never be another global rain like that which produced the Flood, in accordance with God's promise (Genesis 9:11). In spite of their relatively small amount, however, the atmospheric water vapors are quite essential, not only as the immediate source of rain but also as a shield against what would otherwise be lethal radiation from space. They also create a thermal blanket for retention and distribution of the light and heat rays coming to the earth from the sun. The water cycle as it now operates is marvelously effective in all essential respects and offers eloquent testimony to the providential care of God for His creatures, even in the more rugged environment of the postdiluvian world.

The Water of Life

Because of the all-pervasive importance of water in the life of man in the present world, God uses the figure of water to picture the great spiritual truths associated with eternal life. As physical water is essential for physical life, so spiritual life requires "living water," that water given by the Lord Jesus Christ, so satisfying that he who drinks shall "never thirst" (John 4:10, 14). And this water, which springs up eternally, is none other than the Holy Spirit. "He that believeth on Me, as the scripture hath said, from within him shall flow rivers of living water. But this spake He of the Spirit, which they that believe on Him were to receive" (John 7:38, 39, ASV).

The "master of Israel," Nicodemus, had undoubtedly either been in the delegation of Pharisees, or heard their report, when they saw John baptizing in water and heard him say: "He that sent me to baptize with water, the same said unto me, Upon whom thou shalt see the Spirit descending, and remaining on him, the same is He that baptizeth with the Holy Ghost. And I saw and bare record that this is the Son of God" (John 1:33, 34). And when, a few nights later, he went to Jesus to make further investigation, the Lord reminded him of this symbolic import of John's baptism, saying: "Verily, verily, I say unto thee, except a man be born of water and (i.e., 'even') the Spirit, he cannot enter into the kingdom of God" (John 3:5).

Christian baptism in water is thus rich in its spiritual testimony both to those who submit to it and to those who may witness it. It speaks of death to the old life, as did the waters of the Flood, ". . . which also, after a true likeness doth now save you, not the putting away of the filth of the flesh, but the interrogation of a good conscience toward God, through the resurrection of Jesus Christ" (I Peter 3:21, ASV). It thus also speaks of being raised to a new life, as Christ was raised from the dead (Romans 6:3-5). It also symbolizes cleansing from the filth of sin, as water cleanses the flesh. And in its life-giving character the water portrays the pouring-out of the Holy Spirit into the life of the one who receives Christ and is thereby "baptized into one body . . . by one Spirit," and who has been "made to drink into one Spirit" (I Corinthians 12:13).

And finally, since all these blessings are mediated to us through the Word of God, the latter is also symbolized by water. "Christ loved the church, and gave Himself for it; that He might sanctify and cleanse it with the washing of water by the word" (Ephesians 5:25, 26).

New Heavens and a New Earth

"But when that which is perfect is come, then that which is in part shall be done away" (I Corinthians 13:10). When faith becomes sight, when all the promises of the Word have been fulfilled, and when we have entered upon life in all its heavenly fullness, there will no longer be need for the present earth and its atmospheric heavens, and there will be found "no place for them" (Revelation 20:11). "The earth and the works that are therein shall be burned up" (II Peter 3:10). And this must include the most prominent feature of the earth, its "great and wide sea" (Psalm 104:25).

But first, "the sea gave up the dead which were in it" (Revelation 20:13). Also death and Hades delivered up their dead, and then were cast into the lake of fire, and it would have seemed that these two terms should have included all the unsaved dead. Why, then, are the dead in the sea specially mentioned? One immediately recalls the judgment of the great Flood, when the present "sea" was formed, and when "the world that then was, being overflowed with water perished" (II Peter 3:6). Those who perished in the waters of the Flood were wicked in more than the normal sense of the term. "All flesh had corrupted his way upon the earth" (Genesis 6:12), and this corruption was so uniquely pervasive in the soul of antediluvian man that "every imagination of the thoughts of his heart was only evil continually" (Genesis 6:5). The Nephilim, the men of renown, born of the monstrous union of the sons of God and the daughters of men, together with their evil progenitors (Genesis 6:4), have apparently been singled out by God for special condemnation and punishment at the judgment of the great day (Jude 6; I Peter 3:19, 20; II Peter 2:4).

It was specifically the sea which formed the tomb of these beings; in fact, in a sense the sea was formed to be their tomb. It is thus either symbolically or in reality the "prison" of their evil "spirits" (I Peter 3:19). But these, along with all those whose unsaved spirits are in Hades and whose bodies are in the grave, will be given up from their prisons and brought before the great white throne for final judgment according to their works. And when the heavens and the earth are made new, there will be no more sea. But there *will* be a great *lake.* No sea of water, but a lake of fire!

There will, of course, be no further need in that day for the

sea. Water will no longer be needed for cleansing, for there will be
nothing there which is unclean (Revelation 21:27). It will not be
needed to preserve life and to renew the body chemistry day
by day, as at present, for death and the curse are no more. No
longer will the life of the flesh be in the blood, for flesh and blood
do not inherit the kingdom, and the resurrection body will
have no need of blood to maintain its structure (I Corinthians
15:50, 53; Luke 24:39). Men will not need water to quench their
thirst, for "they shall hunger no more, neither thirst any more"
(Revelation 7:16).

Furthermore, all that is now *symbolized* by water will then
have been *realized*. On the one hand, it has symbolized death
and judgment, especially when God's wrath was poured out in
the Flood. And this was made a type of the coming judgment
by fire at the return of Christ (Matthew 24:37-39; II Peter 3:5-7).
As the great sea has been an ever-present reminder of God's judgment by water, so the lake of fire will be an eternal reminder of
God's greater judgment by fire.

On the other hand, water has symbolized eternal life and the
Holy Spirit and the Word of God. Water has been necessary for
life because of the necessity for continual bodily renewal, but
this necessity has really arisen only because of the temporal nature
of the original Creation, and more especially because of the Curse.
And under these conditions, characterized by spiritual death and
separation from God, it has been perfectly appropriate that
water should typify that which would impart spiritual life, the
regenerating work of the Holy Spirit, and the Word of God,
bridging the great gulf of broken fellowship and communication
between God and man.

But in the new earth, the Curse is gone and eternal life is
experienced in all its fullness. No longer need men study the
written Word of God for knowledge of Him, "for the earth shall be
filled with the knowledge of the glory of the Lord, as the waters
cover the sea" (Habakkuk 2:14). In the present time, we can
only "know that we dwell in Him, and He in us, because He hath
given us of His Spirit" (I John 4:13). But then, "we shall ever-
more be with the Lord" (I Thessalonians 4:17).

There *is* water, though, in the new Jerusalem. There is "a pure
river of water of life, clear as crystal, proceeding out of the throne
of God and of the Lamb" (Revelation 22:1). Only one throne,
because God is the Lamb, slain from the foundation of the world.
The fountain of cleansing, opened in the side of the Lamb on
Calvary's cross, when blood and water poured forth, continues
eternally, in a figure, to pour forth the pure river of water of life
from the Lamb on His throne.

This is the river foreshadowed by the first river in Eden which went out to water the garden. These are the "living waters" promised the sinful woman of Samaria, which would be in her a "well of water springing up into everlasting life" (John 4:10, 14). These are the waters offered when Jesus stood and cried: "If any man thirst, let him come unto me, and drink" (John 7:37). And to those who will come out of the great tribulation, the gracious promise is given that "the Lamb which is in the midst of the throne shall feed them, and shall lead them unto living fountains of waters" (Revelation 7:17).

And when Israel shall look in faith upon Him whom they have pierced, there shall be a "fountain opened to the house of David and to the inhabitants of Jerusalem for sin and for uncleanness" (Zechariah 12:10; 13:1). During the millennial reign of Christ, a great river of healing waters, apparently really physical in character, will go out from the temple in Jerusalem (Ezekiel 47:1-12; Zechariah 14:8), but these will also be prophetic of the "pure river of water of life," constituting a visible promise and invitation to those who will inhabit the earth during the thousand years.

Just as, at present, He issues a gracious invitation: "Ho, everyone that thirsteth, come ye to the waters" (Isaiah 55:1). And how wonderfully fitting and compelling it is, that the very latest invitation recorded in the Word of God should come from the lips of the Lord Jesus Himself, as He says: "And let him that is athirst come. And whosoever will, let him take the water of life freely" (Revelation 22:17)!

VIII

THE BIBLE AND THEISTIC EVOLUTION[1]

In introducing the papers in the three-volume work on evolution stemming from the 1959 Darwinian Centennial Convocation in Chicago, Sir Julian Huxley eulogizes Darwin as follows:

Charles Darwin has rightly been described as the 'Newton of biology'; he did more than any single individual before or since to change man's attitude to the phenomena of life and to provide a coherent scientific framework of ideas for biology, in place of an approach in large part compounded of hearsay, myth, and superstition. He rendered evolution inescapable as a fact, comprehensible as a process, all-embracing as a concept.[2]

That this is a realistic appraisal of the status of the theory of evolution in the thinking of modern intellectuals is beyond doubt. Orthodox Christians may not yet be generally aware, however, of the serious inroads evolutionary thinking has been making into Christian theology and Biblical studies in recent years, even in hitherto conservative circles. Theistic evolution has, of course, been generally adopted in modernistic and liberal churches and seminaries for almost as long as Darwinism has been popular among scientists. Fundamentalist and other conservative schools and churches have, for the most part, reacted healthily against these trends and have maintained a vigorous insistence on the full reliability of the Biblical account of origins by special creation.

But especially since the termination of World War II, with the rise of new-evangelicalism and the desire of erstwhile fundamentalists to attain intellectual recognition from the world, no doubt with the sincere desire to win more of the educated classes to conservative Christianity, there has come a continually increasing accommodation to theistic evolution in the thinking of these people.

Dr. J. Frank Cassel, head of the North Dakota State University Department of Zoology, is now President of the American Scientific Affiliation, an organization of some eight hundred evangelical scientists committed to the belief that the Bible is the inspired Word of God. In an article in the A.S.A. Journal, Dr. Cassel says:

Thus, in fifteen years, we have seen develop in A.S.A. a spectrum of belief in evolution that would have shocked all of us at the inception

---

[1]Reprinted from *Torch and Trumpet*, February, 1962.
[2]Julian Huxley: "The Emergence of Darwinism," in *The Evolution of Life* (Vol. I of *Evolution After Darwin*, University of Chicago Press, 1960), p. 1.

of our organization. Many still reserve judgment but few, I believe, are able to meet Dr. Mixter's challenge of, 'Show me a better explanation.' Some may see in this developing view the demise of our organization, but it seems to me that we only now are ready to move into the field of real potential of contribution — that in releasing Truth from the restrictions we have been prone to place upon it, we can really view it in the true fullness which the Christian perspective gives us.[3]

Dr. Cassel, as well as most other leaders of the American Scientific Affiliation, thus are now openly espousing theistic evolution. Dr. Russell Mixter, whom he cites, a former president of the A.S.A., head of the Zoology Department at Wheaton College, has likewise swung largely to the evolutionary viewpoint in recent years. He says:

Genesis 1 is designed to tell *Who* is the Creator, and not necessarily *how* the full process of creation was accomplished.[4]

This is a very popular rhetorical device of theistic evolutionists. But if the only purpose of the Creation account is to tell us that God is the Creator, then what is the value of the rest of the account? Why does not the record simply stop at the end of Genesis 1:1, which gives us this information quite adequately?

If space permitted and if such were the purpose of this article, it would easily be possible to present voluminous documentation of the asserted defection of a large segment of latter-day evangelicalism to theistic evolutionism.[5] Neither the sincerity nor the good intentions of these brethren is questioned, but the writer strongly believes that the long-range results of these defections will prove tragic.

That the theory of evolution, as commonly taught by secular scientists, cannot be harmonized with an acceptance of the Bible, interpreted literally, should be obvious from even a superficial examination. Considerations demonstrating this fact include the following:

(1) The Bible repeatedly states that all things were created in six "days." That these "days" are to be understood in the literal sense is evident from the fact that there is nothing in the context to indicate otherwise; that there is at least one other good

---

[3]J. Frank Cassel: "The Evolution of Evangelical Thinking on Evolution," *Journal of the American Scientific Affiliation,* Vol. 11, No. 4, December, 1959, p. 27.

[4]Russell L. Mixter: "Man in Creation," *Christian Life,* October, 1961, p. 25.

[5]For the purposes of this article, the term "theistic evolution" is taken to include "threshold evolution," "progressive creation" and similar concepts, all of which accept the standard sequence of evolutionary geological ages which is the very foundation of the theory of evolution.

Hebrew word (*olam*) meaning "a long time" which could better have been used here had such been the intended meaning; that in only a negligibly small number of the more than 1300 occasions when the word "day" (*yom*) or "days" (*yamin*) is used in the Old Testament need it have any other than the literal meaning, with such rare instances always being clearly evident from the context; that the word is *never* used elsewhere with a limiting numeral or ordinal (for example, "the first day," "the second day") as it is in nine instances in the Creation narrative, unless it has the literal meaning; that whenever the word "days" appears in the plural, as it does in Exodus 20:11 (". . . . in six days, the Lord made heaven and earth, the sea and all that in them is") and Exodus 31:17, then it always is used with the literal meaning; and from numerous other similar considerations.

(2) The restriction that each of the various kinds of organisms was to reproduce "after his kind" is stated some ten times in the first chapter of Genesis. Although this statement may not preclude variation *within* each kind, it certainly says, if it says anything at all, that there are very definite limits to such variation.

(3) The order of creative events as given in Genesis 1 is substantially different from that supposedly deduced from evolutionary historical geology. Thus, according to the Bible, fruit trees came before fish and other marine organisms. Insects ("creeping things") appeared simultaneously with mammals, birds were developed simultaneously with fishes and sea monsters, vegetation was created before the establishment of the sun and moon, and man was created before woman. All of these things are explicitly contradicted by the accepted order of the fossils in the geologic record, as well as by evolutionary theory.

(4) The references to "evening" (Hebrew *ereb*) and "morning" (Hebrew *boqer*) appearing in connection with each creative day can only reasonably be understood as referring to literal days. These words are used more than a hundred times each in the Old Testament, always in a literal sense.

(5) The Sabbath was emphatically instituted as a memorial of God's *completed* Creation, a fact which is stressed at least four times in Genesis 2:1-3, and is confirmed by Exodus 20:11; 31:17; Hebrews 4:3; 4:10, clearly showing that creation is no longer going on. These Scriptures also plainly show that the processes of Creation were different from the physical processes by which the earth is now maintained (a fact which is also confirmed scientifically by the law of energy conservation, the best established of all scientific laws); thus it is impossible to apply the principle of uniformity, based on present processes, to the elucidation of the events of the Creation period.

(6) There was no death or suffering of sentient life in the Crea-

tion, pronounced by God to be "very good," until after man brought sin into the world and God pronounced a Curse upon the earth (Genesis 3:17; 5:29; Romans 5:12; 8:20-22; I Corinthians 15:21, 22). Therefore, the fossils of dead animals found in the rocks of the earth, which form the very basis of evolutionary geology and the most important of the supposed evidences for evolution, could not have been deposited until *after* the Fall and the Curse, probably largely at the time of the Noachian Deluge.

Such facts as outlined above are increasingly recognized by Bible scholars today, so that the "day-age theory," for harmonizing Genesis with evolution, is not nearly as popular as it once was. A more common device now, reflecting the influence of neo-orthodoxy, is to treat the Creation narrative as a "poem" or "allegory," designed merely to express in dramatic form the great truth that all things originally came from God. In this view, none of the details are to be taken as actual statements of historical fact, but merely as stressing the orderliness and purposefulness of creation.

Obviously, such a method of exegesis will enable one to dispose of any other portion of Scripture which, for one reason or another, he finds distasteful. One wonders why the Holy Spirit bothered to insert so many irrelevant details in the account!

However, the entire Word of God, as recorded in the Holy Scriptures, is a unified whole, and one cannot dispose of one portion without affecting the rest. The Creation account is referred to scores of times in later parts of Scripture, in both the Old and the New Testaments, and always in such a way as to indicate that the writer accepted the Creation narrative as historical fact. Even the Lord Jesus Christ quoted from this account (see Matthew 19:3-6). Thus, denying the historical validity of the Creation account also undermines the authority of the New Testament and of Christ Himself!

Even if one's theology would permit him to adjust whatever passages of Scripture he might find in conflict with evolution, it is still impossible to reconcile theistic evolution with Biblical Christianity. The very nature of Christian morality is squarely opposed to that of evolution. The genius of evolution is the struggle for existence and the attendant extermination of the weak and unfit. It is well known that an evolutionary philosophy is the basis of Communism, Fascism, and the many other anti-Christian systems of the day. The thesis of struggle and self-interest is completely foreign to Christianity, the very basis of which is love and selflessness. It is not possible that a God of love and goodness would institute a universal law that demands continual struggle and hunger and suffering and death.

According to theistic evolution, the divine purpose of evolution was the ultimate creation and redemption of man. How then was it necessary to spend aeons of time in a tortuous drama of evolution to accomplish this purpose? What was the purpose of the trilobites, the dinosaurs, and all the other animals of the distant past, who are said to have lived before man appeared? God is not the Author of Confusion! How could a God of love, looking into the rocks of the earth at the end of the "Day-Ages" of creation, seeing all the fossil evidences of long ages of catastrophe and death, judge it all to be "very good"? No wonder that most of the leaders in evolutionary thought (as quite evident from the Darwinian symposium mentioned above) do not believe in a personal, purposive God!

Carried to the only consistent conclusion, evolution teaches that man has gradually risen from pre-human beginnings to his present state of high development, and will presumably continue to evolve upward in the future. Thus, evolution denies the Fall and therefore the need of a Saviour. In the last analysis, the philosophy of evolution is therefore not only anti-Biblical, but anti-Christian and even anti-theistic.

The supposed scientific basis of evolution, when critically analyzed, is extremely nebulous and contradictory, and has been adequately refuted time and again. The only reason why most people believe in evolution is because "most people believe in evolution" — a kind of mass delusion fostered by group pressure and fear of being thought old-fashioned. The Biblical Christian, in the judgment of this writer, should reject theistic evolution wholly and unequivocally.

IX

SPIRITUAL OVERTONES IN ENGINEERING[1]

By any analysis, the profession of engineering is one of the most dynamic and significant areas of modern life. The great highway networks, high-speed air travel, development of nuclear energy, television, earth satellites, and innumerable other technological facets of the twentieth century are all largely due to the engineering profession.

It is a popular notion that the engineer is a pragmatic, rationalistic, materialistic person, rather lacking in philosophical or cultural interests, and most certainly devoid of spiritual sensitivities and motivations. But this is really only a half-truth. The engineer does have to be logical and conservative, as well as scientific and rationalistic. Perhaps the latter is the predominating theme in engineering, but there are also some very significant spiritual overtones to this theme.

One of these overtones concerns the two absolutely basic and universal principles of science to which all of the engineer's designs must adhere. These are known as the first and second laws of thermodynamics. These two laws have been verified in countless thousands of experiments and, as far as all measurements have been able to show, are universal in scope. They center around the concept of energy, a concept which actually embraces everything in the physical universe. All physical phenomena — even matter itself — are manifestations of energy in one form or another.

The first law of thermodynamics is the law of energy conservation, which. states that no energy can be either created or destroyed, although its temporal form can and does change. In all physical or biological processes energy is being transformed from one form into another. But no energy is ever created in the process!

This means that true creation is not taking place in the present world. And this means that Creation was a finished act of God, completed during some period in the past when a different set of basic principles was being employed by God. God created all things, and then stopped creating.

This is not only a very fundamental principle of engineering, but also a very fundamental principle of all true theology, clearly verified by the Bible. Thus, at the end of the account of Creation in Genesis 1, the Bible says in the opening verses of chapter two:

[1]This article has been reprinted from the January 1963 issue of *Collegiate Challenge*.

94

"The heavens and the earth were finished, and all the host of them. And on the seventh day God ended His work which He had made; and He rested on the seventh day from all His work which He had made."

All the processes of the present order that we have observed conform universally to this principle of energy conservation. On the other hand, the processes employed by God in the Creation period involved bringing energy (and therefore also matter and order) into existence, and thus must have been utterly different from present processes. Consequently, it is completely impossible for man now to use an extension of his knowledge of present processes, based on deductions from this knowledge, to determine the events and sequences of the Creation period. This is the fundamental fallacy in modern evolutionary philosophy.

The only way that man can ever learn anything about the order or nature of the events which took place in the Creation period is for God Himself to reveal them to him. And this is exactly what God has done in the first three chapters of the Book of Genesis.

The second law of thermodynamics is the physical expression of something that has gone wrong with God's creation; although no energy is destroyed, there is always a deterioration of the quality or usefulness of the energy. Things decay, wear out, run down, or grow old. To reverse this process requires the continuous introduction of energy or order from some source outside the system itself.

In engineering, this principle is most noticeable in the ever-present force of friction, which hinders the operation of the machine or process, and always converts some of the usable energy into non-usable heat energy. Much of the engineer's effort is directed toward overcoming these frictional effects as much as possible, but he is never completely successful.

The scientist knows all this is so, but he does not know why, apart from divine revelation. The Bible says that when man sinned, he brought a condition of decay and death into the world. God told Adam, in Genesis 3:17-19: "Cursed is the ground (i.e., 'earth') because of you . . . for you are dust, and to dust you shall return." The Apostle Paul, commenting on this in the New Testament, says: "For we know that the whole creation has been groaning and travailing in pain together until now" (Romans 8:22).

A physical system, left to itself, will eventually convert all its available energy into non-recoverable heat energy and will cease to function. A biological organism, despite a temporary appearance of growth and progress will sooner or later grow old and die.

And any individual person, left to his own devices and without an external source of spiritual strength, will deteriorate and ultimately die spiritually. If one just "lets himself go," he goes down, not up! "Then, when lust has conceived, it brings forth sin: and sin, when it is finished, brings forth death" (James 1:15).

There may be many sources of temporary spiritual or biological or physical stimulation and energizing. But if they are only temporary, they merely delay the process of decay and death. There is only one real source of lasting energy — and that source, of course, is the One who created energy! He has provided a means, entirely by His grace, whereby limitless spiritual energy, and even biological and physical energy, may become available to anyone who sincerely seeks reconciliation to his Creator, and restoration of that fellowship with Him which has been broken by sin.

The Bible reveals that God's only-begotten Son, the Lord Jesus Christ, came into this world-system, to "put away sin by the sacrifice of Himself" (Hebrews 9:26). And Christ is also the source of endless physical life!

"As members of a sinful race all men die; as members of the Christ of God all men shall be raised to life, each in his proper order, with Christ the Very First and after Him all who belong to Him when He comes" (I Corinthians 15:22). His bodily resurrection from the dead, which has been as well verified as any other fact of history, is sufficient surety that those who believe on Him shall also one day triumph over death. "Because I live," said Jesus, "you shall live also" (John 14:19).

One final spiritual overtone has to do with the pragmatic nature of engineering. The engineer cannot base his designs on philosophical speculation or armchair theories. The structure has to be safe; the machine has to function; the process has to work. If available scientific principles are inadequate, which is more often the case than not, empirical tests must be employed for verification purposes.

In like manner, it is perfectly possible to put the claims of Christ and the Bible to empirical test. "I beseech you therefore, brethren, by the mercies of God, that you present your bodies a living sacrifice, holy, acceptable unto God, which is your reasonable service. And be not conformed to this world; but transformed by the renewing of your mind, that you may prove what is that good, and acceptable, and perfect will of God" (Romans 12:1, 2). The promise of God in His Word is: "Believe on the Lord Jesus Christ, and you will be saved" (Acts 16:31).

Many engineers, as well as others from all walks of life, have found this promise empirically true. And no one who has ever really acted upon it, in full assurance of faith, believing in Jesus Christ as Son of God and personal Lord and Saviour, has ever found it to fail. "'O taste and see that the Lord is good: happy is the man that finds refuge in Him" (Psalm 34:8).

X

THE SPIRIT OF COMPROMISE[1]

"How long halt ye between two opinions? If the Lord be God, follow Him: but if Baal, then follow him" (I Kings 18:21).

The spirit of compromise that prevailed among the people of God in Elijah's time also manifested itself in the mid-nineteenth century, as Christians labored to accept both God and evolution, both the Bible and the ages of geology. This was not surprising, for in every age there has been conflict between God and the Devil and a corresponding tension between the world-system and the community of the saints, and always there have been those among the latter who seek to ease the tension by yielding up some of the distinctives of the Bible-founded separatism to which they were called. Neither is it surprising then that the same spirit of compromise is moving strongly today among erstwhile Bible-centered Christians.

This age-long conflict has always been basically the same, although it assumes many forms. On one side there is the omnipotent God, the Creator and the Ruler of the universe. On the other stands a finite creature, who presumes to deny the primacy and sovereignty of God, sometimes explicitly and more often implicitly. The conflict sometimes centers around the doctrine of salvation, whether by grace or works, sometimes over the question of authority, whether the Word of God or the wisdom of men, sometimes over the goal of history, whether the kingdom of God or a humanistic utopia. It is always a question of priority: is the universe God-centered or man-centered? Is our approach to the study of any question to be based on the sovereignty of God and the authority of His revelation, or is it based on the autonomy of the human will and reason?

The idea of evolution did not, of course, originate with Darwin or with his predecessors of the Enlightenment. The revelation of fiat creation *ex nihilo* is essentially unique to the Hebrew-Christian Scriptures. Other traditions or philosophies of origins all visualize development of the world and its inhabitants out of pre-existent materials of some kind. Basically, all such cosmologies are evolu-

---

[1]This paper was originally presented at the joint meeting of the American Scientific Affiliation and the Evangelical Theological Society at Asbury College in Wilmore, Kentucky, on June 20, 1963. It was slightly revised for the *Grace Journal*, and reprinted in the Winter 1964 issue.

tionary, always in opposition to the concept that the eternally self-existent Creator in the beginning brought all things into instantaneous existence out of nothing.

Sometimes the Mosaic cosmogony of Genesis is said to have been written as an accommodation to the culture of the early Hebrews, who were too naive to have understood the idea of evolution. But this is patently absurd, since it would have been far more natural to the Hebrews or any other ancient people to think in terms of an evolutionary origin of things than in terms of special creation from nothing. Evolution is the natural way to explain the origin of things for those who do not know and acknowledge the true God of Creation.

In fact, some kind of evolution is absolutely necessary for those who would reject God. Thus, the idea of an evolutionary origin must have had its first beginnings in the mind of Satan himself, as the only means by which he could rationalize his rebellion against God. The only evidence he had that he was actually a creature of God was the fact that God said so. If he rejected the Word of God, then he must assume that he, along with other beings in the universe and with the non-living components of the universe, and even God Himself, had somehow evolved by innate processes of an eternally-existing universe into their present state. Thus, God's rule may simply have been a coincidence of priority of time of evolution, and might be overcome by a well-planned and executed rebellion.

It is instructive to trace the history of this rebellion throughout human history, as recorded in the Bible. In its essentials it boils down to a conflict between those who worship and serve the Creator and those "who changed the truth of God into a lie and worshipped and served the creature more than the Creator" (Romans 1:25). It is a conflict between God-centered and creature-centered religion. Any sort of religion which denies the Creator the place of absolute primacy and sovereignty in the universe, which prescribes limits of His action or power or which seeks to judge His deeds or His Word at the bar of human reason, is fundamentally a system of evolution. The universe or some aspect or component of it is held to be the focus of ultimate Truth and the idea of God is accommodated, if at all, in some derivative place in the system. This framework appeals to creaturely pride and thus has a strong appeal to fallen men. Acknowledgment of God's absolute sovereignty and man's total depravity, on the other hand, requires complete submission of man's wisdom and will to that of God, and this humiliation is stubbornly resisted by human nature.

Whenever God has created a new thing in the earth, calling out a man or a group of men who are to receive and propagate His Word, Satan has bitterly opposed Him and sought to incite opposition to His word and purposes. Usually, Satan has developed this opposition most effectively through a spirit of compromise on the part of God's people.

Mother Eve was led first to doubt the absolute reliability of God's Word ("Yea, hath God said . . . ") before she fell into overt disobedience. Cain was undoubtedly a religious man, bringing his offering to God, but he did not offer it "by faith," as did Abel (Hebrews 11:4), and Abel's faith, as is true of all genuine faith (Romans 10:17), must have been centered in the Word of God. The inescapable conclusion, therefore, is that Cain brought an offering according to the decision of his own will and wisdom rather than according to the Word of God, and thus he was assuming for himself the prerogative to correct and revise God's Word. He did not reject God's command to bring the sacrifice, but he judged it more expedient and agreeable to bring one which indicated growth and beauty rather than a bloody sacrifice speaking of decay and death.

The antediluvians became so self-centered (note the blasphemous self-assertion of Lamech in Genesis 4:23, 24) and opposed to God (note Enoch's testimony concerning the "hard speeches which ungodly sinners have spoken against Him" as recorded in Jude 15) that the only remedy was complete destruction of mankind and the earth itself by the Deluge. This was not only for the descendants of Cain. The descendants of Seth had eventually compromised with the Cainitic culture to the extent that they were also destroyed and "Noah only remained alive, and they that were with him in the Ark" (Genesis 7:23).

And even then it wasn't long until men again began to reject the Word of the Lord and desired instead to "make us a name" (Genesis 11:4). Because men refused God's Word, therefore, God then confused *their* words and they were scattered. From that day on, the history of the Gentile nations has been predominantly one of spiritual deterioration, as recorded in Romans 1:18-32. "Professing themselves to be wise, they became fools, and changed the glory of the uncorruptible God into an image made like to corruptible man, and to birds, and fourfooted beasts, and creeping things" (Romans 1:22, 23).

And what is idolatry and paganism but evolutionary pantheism? The transcendent Creator is identified with His creation, so that He must be depicted in terms of men or beasts or other created objects. God is a fish, or a cow, or a superman, or the sun, or the elemental forces of nature. He is a part of, and limited by, the universe. He is rejected as omnipotent, sovereign Creator of all things.

In this morass of evolutionary paganism, God spoke to Abraham and called him out to a position of complete separation from the world-system, to establish a new people of God through whom the Word of God might be transmitted. By faith, Abraham believed and obeyed the Word of God. He did not submit the Word of God to his own reason or Chaldean education or to the wise men of Ur, but simply "went out, not knowing whither he went" (Hebrews 11:8), because God had spoken.

But again the spirit of compromise plagued the heirs of Abraham. His nephew and companion, Lot, "pitched his tent toward Sodom" (Genesis 13:12), and though "vexed with the filthy conversation of the wicked," continued to "dwell among them" (II Peter 2:7, 8) until the Lord turned the cities of Sodom and Gomorrah into ashes. Ishmael, the first son of Abraham, turned from his father's position of separation to marry a woman of Egypt. Esau, the first son of Isaac, wed two women of the Hittites. The descendants of Ishmael and Esau have ever since been bitter enemies of the chosen people, Israel.

When God, through Moses, called His people out of Egypt, they complained and longed to turn back time and time again. Once they went so far as to fashion a calf of gold, and call it God, and Moses was forced to make a clear-cut separation of those who were "on the Lord's side," and those who would compromise with the paganism of Egypt (Exodus 32:26).

The period of the judges was characterized by cycles of revival, compromise and apostasy, repeated over and over again. The Israelites for a while would worship and serve the true God, then begin to compromise with the pagan systems of the Canaanite nations, and finally would embrace Baal and Ashtaroth.

Eventually, again through a desire to be more like the surrounding nations, the people of God demanded a human king, and God gave them their request. But the same old cycle of revival, compromise and apostasy continued to operate. The spirit of compromise is always the prelude to apostasy.

The men whom we honor today as the great heroes of faith, on the other hand, are invariably those who stood firm against compromise with the world system of their day, who endured ridicule, suffering and often martyrdom because of their strong faith in the integrity of the Word of God. One thinks of Daniel and his three friends, willing to go into the den of lions or the fiery furnace rather than compromise with the pagan religions of Babylon and Persia — of Nehemiah, rejecting the proffered alliance with the people of the land when building the walls of Jerusalem — of Elijah Josiah, Jeremiah, David, and the other great men of God who firmly believed and acted upon the Word of God in the face of tremendous pressure to compromise and accommodate their stand to public opinion.

Then there are the Christian martyrs, from Stephen on to Wycliffe, and even to those who suffer for their faith today in Siberia, in Red China and other great citadels of modern science and progressivism. All have been men of virile faith in the Word of God, believing that God is able to say what He means and that He means what He says. Apostate or compromising Christians do not fit into this category. They "love the praise of men more than the praise of God" (John 12:43). Like Demas, they "love this present world" (II Timothy 4:10). They would like their "faith . . . (to) stand in the wisdom of men" (I Corinthians 2:5).

The Bible warns in clear terms against this spirit of compromise with the philosophies and systems of the world. It is made emphatically clear that there must always be conflict between the flesh and the Spirit, between the world-system and the believer, between God and the Devil. Only a sampling of the numerous Scriptural exhortations is necessary to demonstrate this.

> Where is the wise? where is the scribe? where is the disputer of this world? hath not God made foolish the wisdom of this world? (I Corinthians 1:20).

> Ye adulterers and adulteresses, know ye not that the friendship of the world is enmity with God? whosoever therefore will be a friend of the world is the enemy of God (James 4:4).

> And be not conformed to this world: but be ye transformed by the renewing of your mind, that ye may prove what is that good, and acceptable, and perfect will of God (Romans 12:2).

> Be ye not unequally yoked together with unbelievers: for what fellowship hath righteousness with unrighteousness? and what communion hath light with darkness? And what concord hath Christ with Belial? or what part hath he that believeth with an infidel? (II Corinthians 6:14, 15).

> And this I say, lest any man should beguile you with enticing words . . . Beware lest any man spoil you through philosophy and vain deceit, after the tradition of men, after the rudiments of the world, and not after Christ (Colossians 2:4, 8).

> O Timothy, keep that which is committed to thy trust, avoiding profane and vain babblings, and oppositions of science falsely so-called: Which some professing have erred concerning the faith (I Timothy 6:20, 21).

> For men shall be lovers of their own selves, covetous, boasters, proud, blasphemers, . . . having a form of godliness, but denying the power thereof: from such turn away (II Timothy 3:2, 5).

> . . . they that are unlearned and unstable wrest, as they do also the other scriptures, unto their own destruction. Ye therefore, beloved, seeing ye know these things before, beware lest ye also, being led away with the error of the wicked, fall from your own stedfastness (II Peter 3:16, 17).

In view of such urgent admonitions and exhortations to the Christian believer (and similar warnings could be multiplied many times from other passages of Scripture), one should be extremely resistant to any spirit of compromise with any of the anti-Christian beliefs or practices of this world-system. And this should be true more than anywhere else in connection with the philosophy of evolution since, as has been pointed out above, this philosophy is really the foundation of the very rebellion of Satan himself, and of every evil system which he has devised since that time to oppose the sovereignty and grace of God in this universe.

Those who advocate a compromising approach to the world do so hoping that this will relieve somewhat the tension between the Christian sphere and that of the non-Christian, and thereby make it easier to win such people to Christ. But, as important and urgent as it is to seek to win men to Christ and the Gospel, it is more important and more urgent to honor God and His Word.

And besides, men are never really won to Christ through compromise, anyway. No one is genuinely saved who imposes certain conditions before he will accept Christ and His salvation. He must come as a helpless child and as a hopeless sinner, trusting fully in the sovereign God for mercy and forgiveness, simply on the basis of the atoning death of His Maker and Redeemer. Compromise has no place in such a transaction as this.

The only reason, therefore, why an evangelical Christian would seek a more intellectually palatable version of the Gospel is that of alleviating its offence. A Christian today can maintain an open and vocal belief in real Creation, in the Fall and Curse, in human depravity, in blood atonement, in salvation by sovereign grace alone and in the coming judgment, only at the cost of suffering ridicule and rejection in greater or lesser degree, by the "intellectual" world. To a Christian with intelligence and ability, as well as ambition, this is very difficult to accept, and often leads him, whether consciously or subconsciously, into a spirit of compromise. And this spirit, of course, has led to numerous and varied devices by which it was thought the Biblical revelation could be harmonized with modern science and philosophy. Basically, all such "harmonies" in one way or another represent accommodations to the theory of evolution, for this is the basis of all anti-theistic movements and teachings.

The only firm and proper ground on which a Christian should stand, however, is the sure foundation of the Word of God, inscripturated in the Bible. It is certain that no one can possibly know anything of the prehistoric past or of the eschatological future with any certainty unless these matters are revealed by God. Science can only speak with certainty on things which *are now*. Science can measure and correlate and evaluate present processes and phenomena, but has no way whatever of knowing that these have always been the same or that they always will be the same. The *principle of uniformity*, which assumes this, represents therefore not a scientific law, but rather an act of faith. But that faith is faith in the eternity of matter, in materialism, in evolution, rather than faith in God and Creation and Revelation. The decision between these two faiths is not a scientific decision, but a spiritual decision, and is therefore made on the basis of moral and spiritual considerations rather than scientific evidence.

If one is willing to recognize that truly reliable knowledge of these matters can come only from God and to accept by faith the proposition that God has revealed them to us in the Bible, then it becomes apparent to the eye of faith that the Biblical framework is wonderfully consistent and satisfying and that the data of empirical science and recorded history all fit perfectly into it. As the Scripture says: "Howbeit we speak wisdom . . .: yet not the wisdom of this world" (I Corinthians 2:6).

This basic Biblical framework, as recorded in Scripture, is built around the following key facts of history: (1) a real and special Creation of all things, *ex nihilo*, in six days, following which God stopped creating; (2) the introduction of rebellion, disharmony, decay and death into the world through man's Fall and God's Curse on the whole Creation; (3) destruction and renovation of the antediluvian earth and its inhabitants at the time of the great Deluge; (4) the work of redemption whereby God Himself became flesh to reconcile the world unto Himself, by His substitutionary death and justifying resurrection; (5) the consummation of God's purposes for the world when Christ returns, involving wrath and judgment for all who have rejected Him, and the creation of a new earth and heavens as the eternal dwelling place of the redeemed.

This basic framework of earth history is emphatically rejected, in every part, by both ancient and modern intellectualism. This rejection is, and must be, based squarely on the assumption of uniformity. The study of present processes could not possibly lead to a knowledge of the above facts of Biblical history, for the simple reason that none of them could possibly be accomplished through present processes.

The study of such present processes is really the only legitimate domain of science. The only processes which can be actually studied and scientifically evaluated are those which are in operation now or which have been in operation within the historic past, as pointed out above. But philosophers have projected these processes into the past and future, on the basis of the premise of uniformity, and have called this projection evolutionary science. It is clearly only philosophy, or even a religion of sorts, rather than a true science, but the highly vocal advocates of this kind of extrapolation have succeeded in persuading many people that "science" indeed has disproved the Biblical framework of earth history.

This, of course, has in essence always been the position of the unbelieving world and so is only to be expected. But the tragedy is that many Christians, even conservative, evangelical Christians, are so intimidated by this pressure that they are willing to compromise the Biblical framework in order to relieve the tension with uniformitarian philosophers. This happened in wholesale fashion in Darwin's generation, and is being repeated in ours. And now, as then, and as has always been true, compromise is but the prelude to apostasy.

Because one compromise merely leads to another, and then to another, until there is finally nothing left to compromise, the Christian must finally go fully over to the position demanded all along by the uniformitarian.

For example, the materialist will insist that geological science has proved the earth to be millions or billions of years in age and therefore that the Biblical record of the creation of all things only a few thousand years ago is in error. The Christian apologist, not wishing to incur the ridicule of the geologists, decides to accept the geological ages as presented, but to insert them in a possible "gap" between the first two verses of Genesis. The original Creation was, he suggests, destroyed by some kind of pre-Adamic cataclysm, and the Creation narrative of Genesis really tells about a "re-creation" of the earth, with its animal and human inhabitants.[2]

But this compromise does not satisfy the geologists. The geological ages, with their purported record of a billion years of gradual and progressive development of all kinds of animals on the earth, including man, simply cannot be so easily disposed of. There is no indication geologically of such a worldwide pre-Adamic cataclysm, for one thing, and furthermore the fossil record preserved in the rocks representing the geological ages is essentially composed of the same kinds of animals as the Genesis narrative describes. The fossil record of man himself is also a part of these supposed geological ages, so that this theory soon leads to some kind of "pre-Adamic man," who lived and died before Adam, even though the Scriptures make it plain (e.g., Romans 5:12; 8:19-23) that death first came into the world as a result of Adam's sin.

---

[2]It is recognized that many Christians have advocated the gap theory on exegetical grounds rather than as a conscious attempt to correlate Genesis with geology. However, it should be recognized that the theory was first put forth about 150 years ago with exactly this primary purpose. Also it should be recognized that the theory, if valid, must be defended on exegetical grounds *only*; it cannot legitimately be offered as a means of reconciling the Bible and the geological ages, for this it does not do.

So it must finally be conceded that the "gap" theory will not really work, geologically speaking, not to mention the many serious Scriptural difficulties it entails. Uniformitarians simply will not accept any such cataclysm and re-creation. Therefore, the evangelical will sooner or later agree that the geological ages must really be contemporaneous with and equivalent to the account of creation and development of the earth and its inhabitants as outlined in the first chapter of Genesis. But, he says, we can interpret the "days" of Creation to be "days of God," rather than literal days. Thus the six days of Creation correspond to the geological ages, during which God was "creating" all things. There are certain admitted gaps in the fossil record, and these correspond to acts of creation; at other times, the created kinds were developing into their various families and genera. This concept we can call "progressive creation," and the Biblical exegesis employed we shall name the "day-age theory."

This seems at first thought to be a very satisfactory way out of the dilemma, but it soon appears that the geologists do not respond with much enthusiasm. They point out that there are so many conflicts and omissions in the Biblical order of events of creation, as compared with the accepted evolutionary order of development in the geological ages, that the Genesis record must still be rejected as far as any historical and scientific accuracy is concerned. And they have a disconcerting way of insisting that the first two chapters of Genesis even contradict *themselves* on the order of creative events. Furthermore, the account of Eve's creation out of Adam seems to make no sense at all from the perspective of the evolutionist. Many of them seem to have a better sense of exegetical propriety than do the harmonistical expositors, recognizing that any system of interpretation which insists on reading "age" for "day," in the absence of any real contextual justification, is merely "wresting the Scriptures" rather than true exegesis. As far as the fossil "gaps" are concerned, they refuse to acknowledge these as evidence of creative acts, but rather continue to hope that the gaps will be continually narrowed and finally closed with increasing knowledge of paleontology and evolutionary mechanisms. And so the "day-age theory" finally proves an inadequate compromise.

So the historical and scientific significance of the Genesis record must be abandoned. But the evangelical now insists that this really doesn't matter after all. The Bible is not a textbook of science, but is a textbook of religion and morals. It merely tells us the "fact" of Creation, and science must discover the method and time in God's other book, the Book of Nature. The Creation record in Genesis is not meant to be taken literally and historically, but is rich in theological truth, teaching man the wonderful fact of divine order and purpose in the universe. Further, there is a wealth of religious significance in the allegory of Creation and the fall of man, even though the events themselves did not actually take place. What difference does it make, they say, to the great doctrines of salvation whether man was a special creation or not, or whether the Flood was universal, or whether Eve was really fashioned out of Adam's side. These are peripheral matters and do not affect our basic Christian beliefs one way or another.

Now surely this compromise ought to be fully satisfactory to the evolutionist. We have adopted fully the interpretive framework that he uses; we can now participate with him as full partners in his research into the mechanisms of evolution, into the evolutionary phylogenies of animals and man, into the investigations of the origin of life itself and the development of the cosmos, and at the same time maintain our faith in the integrity of the Word of God and of the Christian Gospel!

But somehow the evolutionist remains stubbornly unsatisfied with our concessions. If evolution satisfactorily explains all things, he says, why do you insist on bringing religion into the picture? The order that appears in the universe is largely only a construct of our own minds, and anyway it can be explained by chance variation and natural selection; the idea of Design has no scientific utility and is quite unnecessary. As far as Purpose is concerned, there is certainly no evidence in the scientific data themselves, with all their indications of false starts, inversions, extinctions, blind alleys and other facts of evolutionary history, to suggest that any sort of divine Being has any control over, or interest in, the evolutionary process. As Julian Huxley, perhaps evolution's chief protagonist, says:

> Darwinism removed the whole idea of God as the creator of organisms from the sphere of rational discussion . . . Darwin pointed out that no supernatural designer was needed; since natural selection could account for any known form of life, there was no room for a supernatural agency in its evolution . . . There was no sudden moment during evolutionary history when 'spirit' was instilled into life, any more than there was a single moment when it was instilled into you . . . I think we can dismiss entirely all idea of a supernatural overriding mind being responsible for the evolutionary process.[3]

And when it is further realized that the writers of the Bible all seemed plainly to accept the Genesis account of Creation as literally and factually true, as well as the Fall, the universal Flood, and the other great non-uniformitarian events of Biblical history, there is finally no recourse from regarding all the writers of Scripture as subject to cultural limitations and human error in what they wrote.

---

[3] In *Issues in Evolution*, Sol Tax, ed. (University of Chicago Press, 1960), p. 43.

Thus, even Jesus Himself, who frequently referred to and obviously believed in these events recorded in Genesis, must have been fallible in His judgment and limited in His knowledge.

Still further compromise would be necessary if we are to please the real leaders of evolutionary thought, such as Huxley, but we have already gone so far that there is nothing of Biblical Christianity left but a hollow shell. Compromise is a one-way street, ending in a precipice. Its only logical and normal outcome is utter apostasy from the Christian faith, and that is the road that has already been traveled by great numbers of Christian schools, churches, organizations, and publications in this post-Darwin century.

And it is all so tragically unnecessary! The Biblical revelation of origins is wonderfully satisfying, fully self-consistent, and perfectly harmonious with the character and purposes of a sovereign, gracious God. There can never be anything in true science (which really deals only with the *present*) which can ever impugn its literal, historical, factuality. May God in these last days guard His people against this Spirit of Compromise which is today threatening to remove the last vestige of Biblical Christianity even from supposedly Christian America.

The Lord Jesus, looking forward to the time of His return, and seeing the characteristics of the last days, was moved to pose the question: "Nevertheless, when the Son of Man cometh, shall He find faith on the earth?" Perhaps this was meant as a direct question to those who would be professing a faith in Him and His words in those last days. May God grant His people the courage to answer His question: "Amen, Even so, come Lord Jesus."

XI

THE BIBLE *IS* A TEXTBOOK OF SCIENCE[1]

"If I have told you earthly things, and ye believe not, how shall ye believe if I tell you of heavenly things?" (John 3:12).

The Christian polemicist frequently is confronted with the problem of the scientific "errors" in the Scripture, especially in its first eleven chapters. Often he is tempted to resort to the solution of neo-orthodoxy and to protest that "the Bible is, after all, not a textbook of science, but rather of religion. It is meant to tell us the fact of creation, not the method of creation; it tells us who is Creator, not when or how He created. It points us to a confrontation with the Creator, not an understanding of earth history."

It is obvious, of course, that the Bible is not a scientific textbook in the sense of giving detailed technical descriptions and mathematical formulations of natural phenomena. But this is not adequate reason for questioning the objective accuracy of those very numerous portions of Scripture which do deal with natural phenomena and historical events.

This type of apologetic device is both logically unsatisfactory and evangelistically unfruitful. How can an inquirer be led to saving faith in the divine Word if the context in which that Word is found is filled with error? How can he trust the Bible to speak truly when it tells of salvation and heaven and eternity — doctrines which he is completely unable to verify empirically — when he finds that data which *are* subject to test are fallacious? Surely if God is really omnipotent and omniscient, He is as well able to speak with full truth and perspicuity when He speaks of earthly things as when He speaks of heavenly things.

Importance of Basic Presuppositions

It is salutary for anyone dealing with questions of this sort to recognize the essential nature of faith and presuppositions in his reasonings. "Science" (the very meaning of which is *knowledge*) necessarily can deal only with those things which exist at present. The scientific method involves reproducibility, the study of *present* natural processes. When men attempt to interpret the events of the

---

[1]This article appeared in two parts, in the October, 1964 and January, 1965 issues of *Bibliotheca Sacra*.

prehistoric past or the eschatologic future, they must necessarily leave the domain of true science (whose measurements can be made only in the present) and enter the realm of faith.

This faith may be in the doctrine of uniformity, which assumes that these present processes may be extrapolated indefinitely into the past or future and that therefore "all things continue as they were from the *beginning* of the Creation" (II Peter 3:4). If one, because of his basic presupposition, wishes to believe in uniformity in this way, it is logically possible for him to do so and to explain all the pertinent data in this context. He can determine the ages of rocks and suns by projecting present rates of change into the limitless past; he can develop theories about the evolution of species and life and galaxies and chemical elements and everything in the universe, if he wishes, and no one can prove him wrong, for the simple reason that these events are not reproducible and therefore not subject to scientific checking. The most that can be done is to argue that his theories are either probable or improbable on the premise of his own uniformitarian presupposition, depending upon the logical consistency of the superstructure he has erected upon this foundation. But this is all within the context of his pure assumption — his faith — of uniformity.

One can equally logically start with some other assumption and then develop his explanations of the data within that framework. For example, one may assume, if he wishes, that all things in the universe were created by divine fiat five minutes ago. He could say that our apparent memories of earlier events were also created five minutes ago and, once again, no one could *prove* him wrong. He has logically explained all the data that exist, given his initial premise. As a matter of fact, one could assume, if he wishes, that all existence is illusory, a disease of mortal mind. The important point, here, is that one may pretty well believe what he *wants* to believe. He can erect a logical system within which he can explain all the physical data upon any one of any number of mutually exclusive and contradictory premises.

But we are concerned here mainly with the assumption that the Bible is truly *the* Word of God as it claims to be. If one starts with the presupposition that God has written the Bible as His own perfect revelation of the origin, purpose and destiny of the world, then it again is perfectly possible to correlate all the physical data of science and history within that framework. The decision as to which presupposition leads to the most logical and self-consistent system of interpretation must necessarily be based on statistical arguments, and these are notoriously subjective in nature. Thus, in the last analysis, it is a spiritual and moral decision rather than a scientific decision. One can interpret everything in terms of Biblical creationism and catastrophism or in terms of evolutionary uniformitarianism, and all the pertinent data can be understood, at least in broad outline, within the framework of either system. Our concern here is simply to show that the Bible does provide a perfectly sound basis for understanding not only religious truth but also physical processes. It may very effectively serve as a "textbook" of scientific principles within which we can satisfactorily explain all the data of science and history. Whether or not we choose to accept this framework is basically determined by whether or not we *want* to do so. Those who elect the evolutionary framework do so not because the facts of science require this, but because this is the philosophic thought-structure they desire. "They did not *like* to retain God in their knowledge" (Romans 1:28).

The Biblical Framework

Those who, by faith, accept the Biblical cosmogony do so for a perfectly good reason. It is obviously impossible to *prove* that God does *not* exist. There is, at the very least, a good possibility that He does exist. If so, it follows that all things are His creatures. The very minds with which we attempt to develop logical thought-structures are created by Him and must operate within the limitations which He has set upon them. It is therefore necessary, if we would understand anything of the true origin, purpose and destiny of the world and of ourselves, for us to look to God for His own revelation of these things. God can only be known as He wills to be known.

The Bible claims, in numerous ways, to be God's unique revelation. It was accepted as such by Jesus Christ, who also claimed to be God incarnate, and who vindicated His claim by His uniquely perfect life, His atoning death, and especially by His glorious bodily resurrection from death.

The Bible, with this perfect claim to absolute divine authority, does very clearly establish a framework of interpretation within which men are expected to formulate their understanding of the data of science. It is most reasonable and most gracious of God to do so, since it is quite impossible for man, with his study of *present* processes, to know anything for certain about the prehistoric past or the eschatologic future. Only God can *know* these things, and we are able to know the truth about these matters only through faith in God's statements concerning them. Therefore, the Bible-believing Christian goes to the Bible for his basic orientation in all departments of truth. The Bible is his textbook of science as well as his guide to spiritual truth.

In its very structure, in fact, the Scriptures provide fundamental perspective on the entire Bible-science question. The word "Bible" means simply "book," and it is significant that the first mention of "book" in the Old Testament speaks of the "origins of Adam" (Genesis 5:1), and the first mention of "book" in the New Testament speaks of the "origins of Jesus Christ" (Matthew 1:1). The true book, therefore, by implication, is concerned with the first Adam and the second Adam, and the relation between the two. It is also meaningful that the final mention of "book" in the Bible is in Revelation 22:19, speaking of the "book of this prophecy" and the "book of life," with a grave warning against tampering with the words of the Book.

The word "science" is essentially synonymous with "knowledge," and is so used in Scripture. The first mention of "knowledge" in the Bible, in Genesis 2:9, is in connection with the tree of knowledge." One might paraphrase by saying that God warned man against partaking of the "tree of science." There were to be prescribed limits within which man was to exercise dominion over the world; for his own good, he was not intended to venture outside these bounds and know in an experimental fashion the "science of good and evil." By contrast, the first use of "knowledge" in the New Testament, in Luke 1:77, speaks of the "knowledge (Greek, *gnosis*) of salvation," and the final mention speaks of the knowledge of our Lord and Saviour Jesus Christ" (II Peter 3:18).

It is instructive also to compare the words "knowledge" and "wisdom." The former has to do primarily with awareness of facts, whereas the latter has to do with interpretation and correlation and explanation of facts. They are in general parallel to what we mean by our technical words "science" and "philosophy." This also corresponds with their usage in Scripture. In the New Testament, "knowledge" is normally the translation of the Greek *gnosis* or *epignosis*. In one passage, I Timothy 6:20, it is actually translated, in the KJV by "*science*,-falsely-so-called." "Wisdom," in the New Testament, is translated from the Greek *sophia*, which, when compounded with the Greek for "love of," and transliterated into English, becomes "philosophy," the "love of wisdom." It is significant that the only time the actual word "philosophy" is used in the Bible is in Colossians 2:8, which warns: "Beware lest any man spoil you through philosophy and vain deceit, after the tradition of men, after the rudiments of the world, and not after Christ."

True knowledge and true wisdom, which is to say, true science and true philosophy, must come from God alone, and therefore must conform to His framework of revealed Truth. The wise man said: "The fear of the Lord is the beginning of knowledge," and he also said: "The fear of the Lord is the beginning of wisdom" (Proverbs 1:7; 9:10). The Apostle Paul, in a tremendous doxology, shouted: "O the depth of the riches *both of the wisdom and knowledge* of God! how unsearchable are His judgments, and His ways past finding out! For who hath known the mind of the Lord? or who hath been His counsellor? Or who hath first given to Him, and it shall be recompensed unto him again? For of Him, and through Him, and to Him, are all things: to whom be glory for ever. Amen" (Romans 11:33-36).

And he also emphasized that in Jesus Christ, the Living Word of God, "are hid *all* the treasures of wisdom and knowledge" (Colossians 2:3). Not only religious knowledge, but all knowledge; all the treasures of science and true philosophy are hid in Jesus Christ, who is the Creator and Sustainer of the physical universe!

It is not only legitimate then, but absolutely mandatory, for the Christian to depend implicitly on the scientific and philosophic framework revealed in Holy Scripture if he is to attain a true understanding of any of the factual data with which science deals and their implications. It is not surprising at all, then, when we find that the Bible does speak rather explicitly about basic principles in every area of science.

The Physical Sciences

We shall consider science under two very broad categories, the physical sciences and the life sciences, the latter including also the so-called social sciences. The physical sciences include such disciplines as chemistry, physics, geology, meteorology, hydrology, and the like. The life sciences include biology, psychology, anthropology, sociology and others.

As far as the physical, or inorganic, sciences are concerned, perhaps the most fundamental fact concerning them, long ago revealed in Scripture and only recently acknowledged by modern science, is that the physical world is basically non-physical in its ultimate essence. The mechanics of the universe can only be comprehended, and then only vaguely, in terms of non-mechanical, mathematical, concepts.

The Scriptures have made it quite clear that the physical universe was created *ex nihilo* and is fundamentally spiritual in essence. For example, Hebrews 11:3: "Through faith we understand that the worlds were framed by the word of God, so that things which are seen were not made of things which do appear." Some might object that the Greek word for "worlds" really here means "ages." It probably can mean both, but in view of the modern recognition of the universe as a space-matter-time continuum, it would clearly be correct to speak of either space or matter or time or all of them as having been created by the word of God. And the basic "stuff" of this continuum is most definitely not "apparent" to the physical senses.

The same truth is revealed in Hebrews 1:2, 3: "By (God's Son) he made the worlds: Who being the brightness of his glory and the express image of his person, and upholding all things by the word of his power, . . ." Thus, by Power, by the Word, all things were made, and all things are upheld. Jesus Christ, through the continual outflow of His limitless divine energy is thus sustaining all of the material stuff of the universe which He had once created. Here is clearly spelled forth the modern scientific truth of the equivalence of matter and evergy. Here also is revealed the ultimate source of the mysterious nuclear forces, the binding energy of the atom. One might also refer to Colossians 1:16, 17 for the same teaching.

As far as the laws or processes of the physical universe are concerned, these all devolve upon two extremely broad and powerful principles, the so-called first and second laws of thermodynamics. Let it be emphasized that, if there is really such a thing as a *law* of science, these two principles meet that definition. There is no other scientific law supported more fully and certainly by more numerous and meaningful lines of evidence than are these two laws. All physical processes (and all biologic processes, for that matter) involve the interplay of two basic entities called *energy* and *entropy*. One could say that any event occurring in space and time is a manifestation of some form of exchange of energy. The particular event or process basically *is* just this — a transformation of one or more forms of energy (kinetic or motion energy, electrical, chemical, light, heat, sound, electromagnetic, nuclear or other forms of energy) into one or more other forms.

In this process, the *total* energy remains unchanged; no energy is either created or destroyed, although its form may and does change. This is the first law of thermodynamics, the law of conservation of energy. This law has been validated on both the cosmic and subnuclear scales and is a truly universal law, if there is such a thing. And, since energy really includes everything, even matter, in the physical universe, it is as certain as anything can possibly be, scientifically, that no creation of anything is now taking place in the universe, under the normal conditions which science is able to study.

But, in the process, some of the energy is always transformed into non-usable heat energy, and thus becomes unavailable for future energy exchanges. The concept of *entropy* has been developed to describe this phenomenon, entropy being a measure of the unavailability of the energy of the system or process. The second law of thermodynamics describes this by stating that there is always a tendency for any system to become less organized. Its disorder or randomness tends to increase. If isolated from external sources of order or energy or "information," any system will eventually run down and "die."

These laws are basic in every scientific system or process. As far as science has been able to show, they are universal in scope, with no exceptions known. They were only discovered and validated by science, however, about a hundred years ago, after much uncertainty and controversy.

If men had been willing to develop their scientific systems on the basis of Biblical presuppositions, however, it should have been quite obvious all along that the basic physical processes were those of conservation and decay, as now formalized in the statements of the first and second laws of thermodynamics. The Bible does not, of course, state these principles in the mathematical symbols or technical jargon of modern physics but the basic truths are quite clearly enunciated.

The conservation principle is strongly emphasized in the summary statement at the end of the period of Creation, when the Bible says:

> Thus the heavens and the earth were finished, and all the host of them. And on the seventh day God ended His work which He had made. And He rested on the seventh day, and sanctified it: because that in it He had rested from all His work which God created and made (Genesis 2:1-3).

This statement is as clear as it could possibly be in teaching that God's creative acts were terminated at the end of the six days. Whatever processes He may have used in creating and making all His work, ceased when God rested on the seventh day. Nothing is now being created and this is what was finally formalized by science in the first law of thermodynamics.

The most significant implication of this fact, for modern philosophers, is that it is therefore quite impossible to determine anything about Creation through a study of present processes, because present processes are not creative in character. If man wishes to know anything at all about Creation (the time of Creation, the duration of Creation, the order of Creation, the methods of Creation, or anything else) his sole source of true information is that of divine revelation. God was there when it happened. We were *not* there, and there is nothing in present physical processes which can tell us about it. Therefore, we are completely limited to what God has seen fit to tell us, and this information is in His written Word. This is our textbook on the science of Creation!

Present processes are those of maintenance or providence. Not only is nothing being created but also nothing is being destroyed. He is "upholding all things by the Word of His power." By the same omnipotent Word who created all things, "the heavens and the earth which are now, are kept in store" (II Peter 3:7).

But we have already noted another very significant characteristic of all such present processes. It is true that nothing is being destroyed, but it is also strangely true that everything tends to become less useful. This is the second law of thermodynamics, the law of entropy increase, which states that the natural tendency is toward increasing disorder and randomization. Energy tends to become less available for useful work, and the process can only be maintained by a continual influx of fresh energy from outside the system itself. Everything tends to grow old, to wear out, or to run down. There is a universal tendency toward decay and death. And who cannot help but sense that this state of affairs, universal and inexorable though it seems to be, is somehow undesirable and abnormal in a universe created by a Holy and Omnipotent Creator?

But this is all explained and long anticipated in Scripture, which attributes it to the entrance of sin into the world. At the end of the Creation and making of all things, the Bible says that "God saw everything that he had made, and, behold, it was very good" (Genesis 1:31). There was no disorder, no lack of harmony, no decay and, above all, no death in the world as originally made by God. For the Bible-believing scientist, this can only mean that any evidence he finds in the present order of things, or in the records of the past, that indicates disorder and struggle, suffering, decay and death, must necessarily be understood as entering the world after (not before or during) the six days of Creation.

Specifically the Bible tells us that this happened as a result of the sin of the first man, Adam, who had been designated by God as master of the earth and everything in it. When he sinned, God pronounced a Curse on both Adam and his dominion. "Cursed is the earth for thy sake" (Genesis 3:17). And from that day on, as the Scripture says: "the whole creation groaneth and travaileth in pain together until now" (Romans 8:22). The whole world, both the heavens and the earth, and all that in them is, are "waxing old, as a garment" (Hebrews 1:11).

The Life Sciences

The sciences that deal with living matter have not made as much progress as those which deal with inorganic materials. This is partly due to the more complex character of living forms. But probably it is also partly due to the fact that the physical sciences have been developed (even though unwittingly) around the basic physical principles revealed in Scripture, as discussed in the previous section. The life sciences, however, have in the past hundred years been seriously retarded by adherence to the anti-Scriptural and unscientific philosophy of organic evolution. A substantial proportion of the efforts of research workers in these fields has been devoted to fruitless attempts to explain and promote evolution, and these endeavors could have been put to far more productive uses in other aspects of the study of life.

A very interesting anomaly is evident here. Biologists for the most part decry vitalism, vigorously denying that there is any sort of "vital energy" present in organic matter, energy of some radically different nature from the ordinary forms of physical energy. Such concepts as those of "creative evolution," "orthogenesis," "entelechy," and the like are anathema to most life scientists.

It is contended that all organic processes must be explained in terms of chemistry and physics. This means that the basic laws of chemistry and physics (notably the first and second laws of thermodynamics) must be as determinative in organic processes as they are in inorganic processes. These laws postulate quantitative stability and qualitative deterioration, rather than evolutionary growth and development. And this quite clearly indicates that evolution is invalid as a guiding principle in the study of biologic processes. Certainly there may be mechanisms of biologic change, but these changes must be fundamentally degradational in nature.

These facts had of course been previously set forth in Scripture. The essential identification of the physical substance of organic and inorganic matter is clearly indicated. The "earth" was to bring forth grass, herbs and trees (Genesis 1:11), as well as cattle and other living creatures (Genesis 1:24; 2:19). Finally, man's body itself was formed "of the dust of the earth" (Genesis 2:7; 3:19). In other words, the elementary materials out of which the earth was made (which we now know to be the various chemical elements) were also used to make the bodies of living organisms and of man himself. Another very fundamental fact of biologic science revealed in Scripture is that of biogenesis and stability. This fact is generally denied in evolutionary theory, of course, but is nevertheless borne out by the actual data of science. That is, there is no real evidence that the present clear-cut "gaps" between the basic "kinds" of living creatures have ever been crossed or narrowed. Obviously there are many types of biologic differences. No two individuals are ever exactly alike, even when born of the same parents. There is tremendous potential for variation around the fixed locus of each basic kind of animal, leading to different varieties and often to different species and genera, depending upon how these are defined. But never is there any actual evidence that these variations, in either the present or the past, have resulted in changes beyond the limits of the Genesis "kind." If life scientists would only accept this basic fact of science as revealed in the Biblical "textbook," it could be a tremendous boon to further progress in understanding the science of life.

Another important revealed fact, generally rejected by modern anthropologists and psychologists and others dealing with the phenomena of human life, is that man himself is basically distinct from all other types of living creatures. The elements of his body are no different, of course, as we have seen. But man has been created "in the image of God," and this makes all the difference in the world. Perhaps this involves many things, but surely the essential fact is that man has an eternal spirit, capable of fellowship with his Creator.

The "image of God" (Genesis 1:26; 9:6) certainly involves more than the "breath of life," which God breathed into man, because this is shared by other creatures (note Genesis 2:7 in comparison with Genesis 7:21, 22). Perhaps even this much ought to indicate that it will never be possible to understand living matter in terms *solely* of chemistry and physics. Certainly it seems to imply quite strongly that the "breath of life" is of such a different order of phenomena that any hope of man "creating" life is ill-advised, to say the least. Yet how much scientific talent is being wasted in fruitless efforts in this direction!

Experimentation on animals may yield much valuable information on characteristics of the living matter of which human bodies are composed, therefore, but cannot yield correct insight into the behaviour of man himself. The assumption that it *can* yield such information is one of the tragic mistakes of modern behavioural and social science, stemming from the erroneous belief that there is an evolutionary continuity between man and other creatures. If only psychologists and sociologists and others in similar fields would be willing to recognize the basically spiritual nature of man and his behaviour! Since man is made "in the image of God," his actions must be intrinsically connected with this fact and its implications. He has rebelled against the divine fellowship for which he was created, and the behaviour of unregenerate man is fundamentally dependent upon this fact, and not upon chemical and physical phenomena or upon those characteristics of self-consciousness and intelligence which are shared with animals. A real science of human behaviour must necessarily be built upon the great Biblical truths of the Fall, redemption, and reconciliation, and certainly the Bible is our only textbook of these areas of science!

Specific Scientific Disciplines

Thus far we have only been concerned with those broad universals of science that apply in every field of the physical sciences, the life sciences, or both. Now, having recognized that the Bible provides the necessary basic framework for science in general, we can then go on to discern in various parts of Scripture clues to the basic truths of each of the various major specific disciplines in science.

In the field of *astronomy*, for example the Bible clearly teaches the essentially infinite size and variety of the physical universe (infinite, that is, as far as man's measurements or comprehension can extend) which is perhaps the most striking fact of modern astronomy. Isaiah 55:9 compares the vastness of the heavens, for instance, to the vastness of the thoughts of the omniscient God, and Job 22:12 exclaims: "Behold the height of the stars, how high they are!" Jeremiah 33:22, among many other passages, stresses that the stars are so numerous as to be utterly beyond man's ability to count them. I Corinthians 15:41 points out that "one star differeth from another star in glory," and many of the efforts of modern astronomers are devoted to the study and cataloging of the numerous different types of stars.

The basic principle of modern *meteorology* is that of the circulation of the atmosphere. This is quite plainly stated in Ecclesiastes 1:6, which speaks of the "circuits of the winds," for all practical purposes a synonymous term. The very precise proportions of the different components and motions of the atmosphere are stressed in Isaiah 40:12. The essential character of the atmospheric heavens as a sort of terrestrial blanket which makes the earth inhabitable, retaining the heat and spreading the light from the sun, as well as providing air to breathe, is pointed out in Isaiah 40:22, which says that God has "stretched out the heavens as a curtain, spreading them out as a tent to dwell in."

In the field of *hydrology*, which is the science of particular professional concern to this writer, the most basic interpretive principle is that of the hydrologic cycle. This tremendous mechanism, necessary for the maintenance of life on the earth in almost innumerably different ways, provides for the evaporation, transportation, precipitation and run-off of the waters of the earth in a never-ending cycle. This cycle is described with fine accuracy in such Scriptures as Isaiah 55:10, 11; Ecclesiastes 1:6, 7; Job 36:27, 28; Isaiah 40:12; and others. The uniquely great significance of water in the earth's physical and biological processes is implied in Genesis 1:2, 6-10; II Peter 3:5, and many others.

The field of *geology*, including geophysics, geochemistry and its many other subfields, is a science of exceedingly broad scope and importance. The word means "science of the earth" and in one sense could be understood to cover the whole range of science. All of the energy for maintaining geological (and other) processes must come originally from the sun, and this is recognized in such passages of the Bible as Genesis 1:15; Psalm 19:6 and others. The basic principle of isostasy (meaning "equal weights"), which is the foundation of geophysics, is indicated by Isaiah 40:12, which speaks of God "weighing the mountains in scales, and the hills in a balance," from which the pre-eminent importance of gravitational forces in geophysical calculations should easily be inferred. The "shape of the earth" is the peculiar domain of the sub-science of *geodesy,* and the fact of its basic "roundness" is pointed out by Isaiah 40:22. The rotation of the earth is implied in Job 38:12, 14, as well as other places, and the gravitational field of force in Job 26:7.

As far as the stratigraphic order of the rocks of the earth's crust, especially the sedimentary rocks, is concerned, the Bible gives a very important scientific clue which modern geologists have largely chosen to reject or ignore, to the serious detriment of a true science of *historical geology.* This is undoubtedly because this subject is so inextricably bound up with the sacrosanct theory of organic evolution, which requires that the data of historical geology be correlated within a framework of uniformitarianism and evolution. This has led to the concept of the geological ages, extending over many billions of years of imagined earth history. But the Biblical revelation, with its record of a recent Creation of "heaven and earth and the sea and all that in them is" (Exodus 20:11) leads quite directly to the conclusion that at least a great portion of the sedimentary rocks of the crust, especially those containing great fossil deposits, must have been laid down during the days of Noah. God said plainly, in Genesis 6:13, that He would destroy man "with the earth." Job says (12:15) that the "waters overturned the earth," and Peter says that the "world that then was," including the "heavens and the earth which were standing of old by the word of God," was "overflowed with water," and "perished" (II Peter 3:5, 6). Assuming the Biblical revelation to be true, there is no reasonable conclusion possible other than that the Flood must serve as the main vehicle of interpretation in developing a valid science of historical geology. The rocks themselves give abundant evidence of aqueous catastrophism in their formation, and the difficulties that may be encountered in developing a so-called "flood geology" are actually far less serious than those which can be lodged against uniformitarian geology. The latter, as previously indicated, is both the support and the result of the theory of organic evolution, and this theory is utterly impossible in terms of the basic laws of conservation and decay.

The science of *paleontology* is deeply involved here also. The fossils in the sedimentary rocks, which provide the basic data of this discipline, have been used to erect the interpretive structure of evolutionary historical geology. But these very fossils speak quite eloquently of disorder and death in the world, and very often speak of sudden, aqueous death. God has plainly revealed to us that these conditions resulted only from the entrance of sin into the world when Adam rebelled against the Word of God, with the resulting Curse pronounced on his dominion. Thus these data of paleontology can only legitimately be interpreted in terms of judgment and catastrophe, not in terms of evolutionary progress.

The science of *physiology* can well be understood as centered around the wonderful Biblical statement that "the life of the flesh is in the blood" (Leviticus 17:11). Basic truths of psycho-therapy are intimated in such Scriptures as Proverbs 16:24 and 17:22.

In similar fashion, one could examine the sciences of *archaeology, anthropology, medicine, taxonomy,* and others, and again and again one could find that the basic principles are revealed in Scripture. The detailed data and formulations are of course not given; the discovery of these is man's responsibility as set forth in the great command to "subdue the earth," given when man was first created (Genesis 1:28). But the basic principles for interpreting and correlating and utilizing these data *are* given. To the extent that man has worked within the interpretive framework provided by revelation, his science has been productive and beneficial to mankind. Otherwise it has proved sterile and often even harmful.

In the final analysis, all truth is one. God did not create one universe of physical reality and another of spiritual reality. The same God created all things, and His Word was given by His Holy Spirit to guide us into *all* truth. The Bible is, for the Christian, *the* textbook of science and of all knowledge.

XII

THE POWER OF ENERGY[1]

This title may at first disturb the disciplined scientific mind because of its apparent dimensional inconsistency. As a matter of fact, for our present purposes, it might just as well be titled "The Energy of Power." The point to be made, in either case, is that *energy*, as a concept, is tremendously powerful, both in the solution of technical problems and in its implication with reference to the true understanding of nature and the universe. And this is true whether we are speaking technically of energy or its time-derivative, power. Neither is an actual physical substance, of course, but each is an extremely useful and significant concept, without which the great contributions of modern science could hardly have been possible. Dr. R. B. Lindsay, Director of the Ultrasonics Laboratory at Brown University and Dean of its Graduate School, says:

> Of all unifying concepts in the whole field of physical science, that of energy has proved to be the most significant and useful. Not only has it played a major role in the logical development of the structure of science, but, by common consent, it is the physical concept which has had and still has the widest influence on human life in all its aspects. Under the prevailing misnomer 'power,' it is the stock-in-trade of the engineer and that which makes the wheels of the world go round. . . . the interpretation of phenomena in terms of the transfer of energy between natural systems is the most powerful single tool in the understanding of the external world.[2]

The power of the energy concept is implicit in the two great laws of thermodynamics, which are without question the two most basic and securely founded of all the laws of physical science. All real processes in the physical or biologic realms necessarily involve transformations of energy from one form into another. The first law of thermodynamics, that of energy conservation, expresses the quantitative equivalence of total energy before and after the transformations. The second law, that of energy deterioration, states that in the process some of the energy must be transformed into non-recoverable heat energy — not destroyed, but rendered unavailable for use. In terms of "entropy," which is merely a measure of the non-availability of the energy of a system, any

---

[1]Reprinted from the *Creation Research Society 1964 Annual*, pp. 18-23.
[2]Lindsay, R. B. "Concept of Energy in Mechanics," *Scientific Monthly*, October 1957, p. 188.

natural process or transformation of energy in a closed mechanical system, necessarily involves an increase in the entropy of the system. According to the great Harvard physicist, P. W. Bridgman:

> The two laws of thermodynamics are, I suppose, accepted by physicists as perhaps the most secure generalizations from experience that we have. The physicist does not hesitate to apply the two laws to any concrete physical situation in the confidence that nature will not let him down.[3]

The universal validity of the first law, that of energy conservation, is also indicated by Gerald Feinberg and Maurice Goldhaber:

> The physicist's confidence in the conservation principles rests on long and thoroughgoing experience. The conservation of energy, of momentum, and of electric charge have been found to hold, within the limits of accuracy of measurement, in every case that has been studied. An elaborate structure of physical theory has been built on these fundamental concepts, and its predictions have been confirmed without fail.[4]

With respect to the second law, the following evaluation by A. R. Ubbelohde is typical:

> In its most modern forms, the Second Law is considered to have an extremely wide range of validity. It is a remarkable illustration of the ranging power of the human intellect that a principle first detected in connection with the clumsy puffing of a steam engine should be found to apply to the whole world, and possibly even to the whole cosmic universe.[5]

It would be difficult to point to any of our basic methods or formulas in any branch of mechanics or engineering which are not intimately related to these energy requirements. Though the working scientist or engineer may be inclined to overlook them, being engrossed in a tangle of technical details and specific procedures, he will find that both his techniques and basic insights will be greatly strengthened if he maintains a continual awareness of the fundamental energy relationships to which his designs and decisions must conform.

It is not too surpising, then, to find that these relationships and the very concept of energy itself lead to tremendous inferences far beyond the realm of mechanics and thermodynamics to which they were first applied. The basic nature of "energy" or "power" is still enveloped in mystery. Energy can appear in many quantita-

---

[3]Bridgman, P. W. "Reflections on Thermodynamics," *American Scientist,* October 1953, p. 549.

[4]Feinberg, Gerald and Goldhaber, Maurice. "The Conservation Laws of Physics," *Scientific American,* October 1963, p. 36.

[5]Ubbelohde, A. R. *Man and Energy,* New York, George Brazillier, Inc., 1955, p. 146. Ubbelohde is Professor of Thermodynamics at the Imperial College of Science and Technology of the University of London.

tively interchangeable forms — electrical energy, chemical energy, sound, heat, light, pressure, magnetic energy, mechanical energy, etc. And one of man's greatest scientific discoveries has been that of the identification of matter itself as merely one form of energy, so that the law of mass conservation becomes only a special case of the law of energy conservation, and matter becomes under the proper conditions interconvertible with other energy forms.

Since all the physical universe, including matter, is ultimately energy, and since energy can be neither created nor destroyed, according to the conservation principle, the inference is that the totality of energy in the universe has never changed since its origination. Either the universe has always existed in its present state (and this is contradicted by the second law of thermodynamics), or it was at some time in the past brought into its present state, necessarily by means of laws or principles not now operative in the universe. Once these latter laws were superseded by the present conservation-deterioration laws, there could have been no additional creation or destruction of the physical stuff of the universe.

This fact is not obvious from a superficial examination of nature, which exhibits numerous cases of *apparent* causeless origins and *apparent* increases of order, reflected in the many crude notions of spontaneous generation and evolution held by ancient philosophers. The conservation law has only been accepted within the past 120 years, after much scientific labor and against much opposition. It is remarkable, therefore, that in the first chapter of Genesis, following the familiar Biblical account of Creation, appears the following:

> Thus the heavens and the earth *were finished,* and all the host of them. And on the seventh day God *ended His work which He had made;* and He *rested* on the seventh day *from all His work which He had made* (Genesis 2:1, 2).

With reference to the energy balance of the earth, which of course depends almost wholly upon the influx of solar radiant energy, the further significant statement is made that the function of the sun, relative to the earth, was: ". . . to give light upon the earth" (Genesis 1:17).

Whether or not the writer understood the significance of this assertion, the fact remains that the sun's "light," or radiant energy, provides all the earth's usable energy except that of its own rotation and the nuclear energy of its atomic structure. The sun's light maintains the physical and biologic life of the earth. It has been calculated[6] that all of the stored-up energy sources of the earth —

---

[6]Ayres, Eugene and Scarlott, Charles A. *Energy Sources,* McGraw-Hill Book Company, (1952) p. 186.

124 Studies in THE BIBLE AND SCIENCE

its coal, oil and gas reserves, its peat and timber, even its fissionable uranium, would only suffice to keep the earth going for about three days if the sun's energy were to be cut off!

The energy of light, in fact, may be considered as the most basic of all the forms of energy. It includes all radiant energy, from the X-rays and cosmic rays and other short-wave-length radiation at one extreme, through visible light, heat, and the electro-magnetic rays at the opposite end of the spectrum. The energy of matter is basically light energy, with matter and energy related by the Einstein equation through the fundamental and universal constant of the velocity of light. The first creative command of God, according to the Genesis record, is thus very significantly said to have been: ". . . Let there be light: and there was light" (Genesis 1:3).

The energy conservation law is occasionally said not to have proved universally successful when applied to phenomena on the sub-atomic scale. Quite possibly this is because of the still very incompletely understood nature of these phenomena, and in fact the somewhat still mysterious relation between matter and energy. Of course, this area of investigation is so complex and specialized and so rapidly changing that no one but a very up-to-date nuclear physicist should hazard any definite statement about the basic significance of nuclear phenomena.

However, within the accuracy of all pertinent experimental evidence, it is true that the energy conservation principle has been demonstrated true on the sub-nuclear scale no less than on the scale of ordinary experience. As Feinberg and Goldhaber have recently pointed out:

> Thousands of laboratory experiments, performed in different ways and measuring all the quantities involved, have confirmed that the laws of conservation of energy and momentum do hold true in the domain of elementary particles. . . It is clear that the laws of conservation of energy and momentum, introduced . . . to describe collisions between macroscopic bodies, also apply with remarkable accuracy to the collisions and interactions of sub-atomic particles.[7]

One thing is certain, and that is that the energies associated with the various nuclear particles are tremendous and, when partially converted into other forms of energy through nuclear fission or thermonuclear fusion processes, the physical effects can be cataclysmic. The source and nature of the binding energy that normally maintain the integrity of the atomic structure against the powerful electrical forces tending to disintegrate it are yet

[7]*Op. cit.*, pp. 39, 42. Dr. Feinberg is Associate Professor of Physics at Columbia University, and Dr. Goldhaber is Director of the Brookhaven National Laboratory.

quite uncertain, although many of its characteristics have been determined.

As the physicist R. E. Peierls says:

> The next fundamental problem that arises is that of the nature of the forces which hold the neutrons and protons in a nucleus together . . . the attractive energy that holds any one particle in the nucleus is, in general, of the order of 6 to 8 million volts . . . to obtain the precise laws of the nuclear forces is one of the central problems of nuclear physics, which is not, as yet, completely solved.[8]

And the problem today seems as far from solution as ever. As modern research has thrown more and more light on the nature of the nucleus, with its various sub-nuclear particles, the more complex does its nature seem to be. Even if its physical character is eventually completely understood, its basic origin and source would still be at best a matter of pure speculation. Peierls admits:

> Even if one day we find our knowledge of the basic laws concerning inanimate nature to be complete, this would not mean that we had "explained" all of inanimate nature. All we should have done is to show that all the complex phenomena of our experience are derived from some simple basic laws. But how to explain the laws themselves.[9]

Another quite remarkable assertion of the Scriptures is pertinent here. The writer of the Epistle to the Hebrews mentions that having first made the worlds, God (through His Son) now is continually "upholding all things by the word of His power" (Hebrews 1:3). A legitimate paraphrase of the Greek original here would be that He is "maintaining the physical integrity of the matter of the universe by means of the continual efficacious outflow and outworking of His innate infinite reservoir of basic energy."

The same intimation of the maintenance of the integrity of matter by a certain basic and primal form of energy (and therefore of the essential equivalence of matter and energy) is suggested also by St. Paul, when he says:

"In Him [i.e., Christ] all things hold together" (Colossians 1:17).

and by St. Peter, who says that:

". . . the heavens and the earth which are now, by the same word are kept in store" (II Peter 3:7).

But the full import of the energy concept cannot be grasped

---

[8]Peierls, R. E. *The Laws of Nature*, New York, Charles Scribner's Sons, (1956) p. 240.

[9]*Ibid.*, p. 275. Peierls is Professor of Mathematical Physics at the University of Birmingham in England, and a Past President of the Atomic Scientists Association.

until we consider also the second law of thermodynamics. In any closed system, in which energy transactions take place, the availability of the energy for the performance of useful work must always decrease. The total energy remains unchanged, but its usefulness has decreased.

This physical phenomenon is not at all obvious on the surface of things and had to overcome much opposition before it became generally accepted as scientific truth. It seemed to contradict the philosophy of progress and developmental evolution. Nevertheless, the brilliant theoretical and experimental researches of Carnot, Clausius and Lord Kelvin, followed by numerous others in more recent decades, have definitely proved this second law to be of essentially equal validity with the first. In recent times, it has even been possible to analyze and predict in some cases actual rates of energy dissipation (or entropy increase). This sort of study, of course, becomes of great practical importance in engineering design and analysis. Energy dissipation is often of paramount importance in the mechanics of the conversion process and its efficiency, and therefore in its cost of operation. The second law of thermodynamics precludes the design of any process or machine 100% efficient, as well as any sort of perpetual motion device.

Because of the historical background, it has been customary to think of these two laws of thermodynamics as more or less interdependent. However, there does not seem to be any necessary connection between them. The fact that the totality of energy remains constant does not in itself imply at all that its availability should continually decrease. In fact, there now exists a considerable body of evidence that this so-called second law of thermodynamics is only a particular application of a much more general law which deals not only with the phenomena of physical energy but also with many other categories of phenomena in the physical, biological and perhaps even in the psychological and sociological realms. This broader law has been called, by the British physicist, Dr. R. E. D. Clarke, the "law of morpholysis,"[10] a term derived from two Greek words, and meaning simply "loosing of structure."

This term seems admirably adapted to describe a very important and apparently universal phenomenon, namely that there always exists a tendency in nature towards disorder or disorganization. The law of morpholysis merely formalizes the everyday observation that any evidence of order or organization requires some sort of explanation to account for it, whereas anything exhibiting randomness or disorder or heterogeneity is per se "natural"

---

[10]Clarke, R. E. D. Darwin: Before and After, Paeternoster Press, London (1948) p. 150.

and does not call for any explanation as to how it was thus arranged. The natural tendency is always from the state of maximum improbability to that of maximum probability, from the organized to the disorganized. Any sort of ordered arrangement requires some sort of external agency to bring it about. Harold F. Blum, Professor of Biology at Princeton, says:

> All real processes go with an increase in entropy. The entropy also measures the randomness or lack of orderliness of the system, the greater the randomness the greater the entropy; — the idea of a continual tendency toward greater randomness provides the most fundamental way of viewing the second law . . .[11]

Even from an engineering viewpoint, this is now recognized as the real significance of the second law of thermodynamics. This concept of entropy explains energy deterioration in terms of decreased order of molecular or atomic structure. In discussing the entropy concept and some of its newer applications, Dr. W. L. Everitt, Dean of Engineering at the University of Illinois and past president of the American Society for Engineering Education, points out that:

> . . . it may be inferred that entropy is a measure of randomness, confusion, or lack of organization. Such a term can be applied not only in a thermodynamic sense, but also to information problems.[12]

This tendency toward disorder is of course apparent in many realms beside that of energy dissipation. There is the phenomenon of aging and death in living creatures, for example, still very incompletely understood but apparently related to the breakdown of complex and unstable protein molecules into simpler and more stable ones, less able to transmit free energy for biologic processes.

Similarly, the primary mechanism of biologic evolution of species, that of mutation of genes in the germ cells, operates when some disorganizing medium such as short-wave-length radiation, certain powerful chemicals, etc., penetrate the germ cell and disturb its previously highly organized chemical structure. The reshuffling of genetic factors thus induced would nearly always decrease its degree of order and organization and therefore result in a less viable and efficient organism. This is why almost all, perhaps all, mutations are either lethal or harmful to the creatures experiencing them, in their struggle for existence. This is supported by no less an authority than Dr. H. J. Muller, perhaps the world's outstanding living geneticist and authority on mutational mechanics:

---

[11]Blum, Harold F. *Time's Arrow and Evolution*, New York, Harper and Brothers, (1962), p. 15.

[12]Everitt, W. L. "Empathy and Entropy," *Journal of Engineering Education*, April 1957, p. 658.

It is entirely in line with the accidental nature of natural mutations that extensive tests have agreed in showing the vast majority of them to be detrimental to the organism in its job of surviving and reproducing, just as changes accidentally introduced into any artificial mechanism are predominantly harmful to its useful operation. According to the conception of evolution based on the studies of modern genetics, the whole organism has its basis in its genes. Of these there are thousands of different kinds, interacting with great nicety in the production and maintenance of the complicated mechanism of the given type of organism. Accordingly, by the mutation of one of these genes or another, any component structure or function, and in many cases combinations of these components, may become diversely altered. Yet in all except very rare cases the change will be disadvantageous, involving an impairment of function.[13]

It is probable that such mutational deteriorations account for many phenomena of paleontology and morphology, such as vestigial organs and the fact that most modern creatures are represented in the fossil record by larger and more highly developed individuals than their modern counterparts. Mutation, isolation, inbreeding, etc., also may account for the historical deterioration of once virile sociological units of peoples and cultures, encountered so frequently in the study of history.

But it is the cosmological implication of morpholysis that is of greater significance. If the entropy or disorder of any closed system must continually increase, and since the universe may be regarded as a very large, but finite, closed system, it follows that the universe as a whole is becoming progressively more disordered. Its reservoir of physical energy is continually degrading, tending ultimately to a state where all energy will have deteriorated to unavailable heat energy. The universe, in other words, is "running down"; it is growing old, wearing out.

It cannot, therefore, be infinitely old; if it were, it would already have attained this state of maximum entropy. It must have had a beginning. If it is growing old, it must once have been young; if it is wearing out, it must have once been new. A universe now running down must first have been "wound up."

This is the inexorable conclusion of the second law, unless one is disposed to assert a continual evolution of fresh matter or energy out of nothing somewhere in space (according to the theory of Fred Hoyle and others) or to insist that the universe is pulsating, with the entropy as periodically reversed to permit its rewinding. Neither of these alternatives, of course, is supported by a shred of *direct physical evidence*, but only by as-

[13]Muller, H. J. "How Radiation Changes the Genetic Constitution," *Bulletin of the Atomic Scientists,* paper prepared for the U.N. Conference on Peacetime Uses of Atomic Energy, at Geneva, 1955.

sumptions as to what, in the judgment of their proponents, the nature of things *ought* to be.[14] On the other hand, there is literally a tremendous mass of direct physical evidence supporting the entropy law.

However, these alternate hypotheses do point up one fact, namely that the morpholysis principle is not inherent in the basic nature of things. The very fact that men of intellect can conceive and support alternative theories proves this. This tendency toward disorder seems somehow, intuitively, to be an unwelcome intruder into the ideal nature of things, something that *ought not to be,* but which nevertheless *is.* Just *why* this deteriorative principle is an apparently universal law is seemingly beyond the reach of scientific discovery.

But here it is possible that the Scriptures, already seen to contain remarkable intimations about the fundamental nature of things, may again have something significant to say. The basically spiritual nature of energy has already been inferred, so that the principle of deterioration of energy may likewise involve spiritual overtones.

Thus, the Christian doctrine of the Fall of man and the resultant Curse of God on His Creation, as taught in Genesis 3:17-19,[15] although often rejected as mythological by modern intellectuals, is able to provide at least a causal explanation for the universal phenomenon of morpholysis. At the same time, it refutes the hopelessly pessimistic future of the universe implied by the second law of thermodynamics by reminding us that He who established the Creation and who later imposed upon it the Curse of corruptibility and decay, is yet Himself outside the Creation and therefore not subject to its laws. For example, quoting again the author of Hebrews, who in turn is quoting Psalm 102:

> And, Thou, Lord, in the beginning hast laid the foundation of the earth; and the heavens are the works of Thine hands: They shall perish; but Thou remainest; and they all shall wax old as doth a garment; And as a vesture shalt Thou fold them up, and they shall be changed: but Thou art the same, and Thy years shall not fail. (Hebrews 1:10-12)[16]

A future time when the Curse shall be removed from the earth and when, therefore, the law of morpholysis will presumably be "repealed" is often promised in Scripture. In the classic eighth

---

[14]See, for example, the cogent criticsm of theories of this kind in an article by Dr. Herbert Dingle, Professor of the History and Philosophy of Sciences at the University of London, "Cosmology and Science," *Scientific American,* September 1956, pp. 224-236.

[15]See also Romans 5:12, I Corinthians 15:21, 22.

[16]See also I Peter 1:24, 25; Matthew 24:35; Isaiah 51:6, etc.

chapter of Romans, said by Martin Luther to be the greatest
chapter in the Bible, St. Paul says:

> For the Creation was made subject to vanity, not willingly, but by
> reason of him who hath subjected the same in hope. Because the
> Creation also shall be delivered from the bondage of corruption
> (literally "decay") into the glorious liberty of the children of God.
> For we know that the whole Creation groaneth and travaileth in
> pain together until now (Romans 8:20-22).[17]

But for the present we must continue to live with the entropy
principle. The engineer must continue to design his machine or
process with full allowance for the effects of energy dissipation.
Great strides are being made in the broader application of these
concepts of energy conservation and deterioration, in atomic energy,
computers and automation, rocketry, inertial guidance, and even
in such fields as information theory. A more incisive and inclusive
understanding of the real character of the second law, especially, will undoubtedly result in still more remarkable technological
advances, in probably every area of science.

But one cannot help but sense a danger, even perhaps a
probability, that new scientific and technological break-throughs
may, as has often been true in the past, only accelerate the
sociological and moral morpholysis. Energy and entropy are,
we repeat, basically non-material, even spiritual, in essence.

As to sources of strictly physical power, it appears that the
so-called Christian West is rapidly being overwhelmed by the
anti-Christian forces of the world. In manpower, it has long been
obvious that the West is immensely inferior. In potential energy
sources, considering the vast and largely untapped resources of
Russia, Asia, and probably Africa, the reservoir of the East is
again far larger than that of the West. Even in the non-material
resources of intellectual and moral power, there is no little evidence today that the Eastern peoples are at least the equals of
those in the free world.

In a day and age in which the balance of power in a technological
sense has been superimposed upon the old concept of the balance
of power in a military sense as determinative of the world's
future, we have suddenly come to realize that our Western delusion of perpetual superiority may be tragically unrealistic. Evidences are multiplying that the true balance of power in the
world henceforth may favor those forces that are being arrayed
in opposition to us.

But there does remain one largely unused source of power,
access to which is more to be valued than all others combined.
The One who inhabits eternity, Who has created and Who "up-

---

[17]See also Revelation 21:1, 4; 22:3; Isaiah 66:22; II Peter 3:13.

holds all things by the word of His power," is Himself the source of all physical, intellectual, moral and spiritual energy. Access to this spiritual power (and often even to physical and intellectual strength) is obtained through prayer and a Christ-centered faith, according to the testimony both of Biblical revelation and of millions of individual Christians across the centuries, including the writer of this paragraph. In the words of St. Paul:

> For I am not ashamed of the gospel of Christ, for it is the *power* of God unto salvation, to everyone that believeth. . . (Romans 1:16).

Therefore, for instruction in the matter of power sources for those who deal in science and technology, for insight into the universal significance of the concepts of energy and power, for encouragement to all who are disturbed over world conditions, and for personal exhortation to those individuals who would seek for roots in eternity, we close with the words of Him, who, after dying in atonement for the sins of fallen man and then after winning the ultimate triumph over the universal rule of decay and death by His bodily resurrection from the tomb, could say with all assurance:

> . . . *All power* is given unto me in Heaven and in earth. . . . And, lo, I am with you alway, even unto the end of the world. Amen (Matthew 28:18, 20).

XIII

NOAH'S FLOOD[1]

And Its Significance

According to the scriptures, the great deluge in the days of Noah was a worldwide catastrophe, in which "the world that then was, being overflowed with water, perished" (II Peter 3:6). If the Biblical account is reliable and meaningful, then the Genesis Flood must have much significance for modern science and theology. But, to their serious loss, most scientists and Biblical scholars today either reject or ignore this witness.

That the Bible actually *does* teach a universal flood, rather than a local or regional flood of some kind, is evident for many reasons, among which are the following:

1. The flood waters covered the mountains (Genesis 7:19, 20), and continued to cover them completely for about nine months (Genesis 8:5). These facts can answer hydraulically to a worldwide flood and to nothing else.

2. Expressions of universality in the account (Genesis 6-9) are not scattered and incidental (as is the case elsewhere in Scripture when apparently universal terms are used in a limited sense), but are repeated and emphasized again and again, constituting the very essence of the narrative. This writer has counted at least 30 times in which this universality ("all flesh," "every living thing," "all the high hills under the whole heaven," etc.) is mentioned in these chapters.

3. The worldwide character of the Flood is also assumed in later parts of Scripture. See especially the testimony of the Psalmist (Psalm 104:6), of Peter (I Peter 3:20; II Peter 2:5; 3:5, 6), and of the Lord Jesus Christ (Matthew 24:37-39).

4. The primary purpose of the Flood was to destroy all mankind. This is seen not only in the numerous statements in Genesis to that effect, but also those of Peter (II Peter 2:5), and of Christ (Luke 17:26, 27). This could hardly have been accomplished by anything less than a global catastrophe. The wide distribution of early man is indicated by anthropological studies, but of even greater significance is the Biblical testimony concerning the extreme longevity and productivity of the antediluvians, who had been "filling the earth" for hundreds of years (Genesis 1:28; 6:1, 11).

---

[1]Reprinted from *Good News Broadcaster*, July-August, 1965, pp. 8-10.

5. The tremendous size of the Ark (which, according to the most conservative calculations, had a volumetric capacity equivalent to that of over 500 standard railroad stock cars) is an eloquent witness that far more than a regional fauna was to be preserved therein. Its purpose was "to keep seed alive upon the face of all the earth" (Genesis 7:3), quite a pointless provision if the deluge was local.

6. There would obviously have been no need for an ark at all if the Flood were anything other than universal. Noah and his family could far more easily have migrated to some distant land during the 120 years it took to build the Ark. Similarly, the birds and animals of the region could much more simply have been preserved by a process of migration. The Flood narrative is thus made entirely ridiculous by the local-flood hypothesis.

7. God's thrice-repeated promise (Genesis 8:21; 9:11, 15) never again to "smite every thing living" by a flood clearly applies only to a universal catastrophe. If the promise referred only to a local flood, it has been repeatedly broken every time there has been a destructive flood anywhere in the world. The local-flood notion therefore not only charges Scripture with error, but maintains that God does not keep His promises!

Biblical Christianity treads on dangerous ground when it allows scientific difficulties to dilute this plain and emphatic Bible teaching of the historical fact of a universal flood in the days of Noah. Rejecting or neglecting this fact means rejection of not only the Genesis record but also the New Testament's testimony about that record.

On the other hand, acceptance of the Flood as universal, immediately leads to scientific implications of profound importance. For instance, the waters for such a flood can only have come from either great upheavals of the ocean basins or from an atmospheric source entirely different from the grossly inadequate vapor content of the present atmosphere. The Scriptures attribute it to both sources. The torrential rains, continuing for 40 days and nights (Genesis 7:12), and in perhaps lesser intensity for 110 more days, in all probability resulted from condensation of the extensive vapor blanket implied by the "waters above the firmament" of Genesis 1:6-8. The simultaneous "breaking-up" of "all the fountains of the great deep" (Genesis 7:11) undoubtedly involved volcanic and tectonic upheavals of the earth's crust and subterranean waters, and this also continued for 150 days (Genesis 7:24; 8:2, 3).

Small wonder that the Apostle Peter says that "the world that then was, being overflowed with water, perished." That "world," of which he spoke, included both the earth and the atmospheric heavens (II Peter 3:6), and they were evidently completely different from "the heavens and the earth, which are now" (II Peter 3:7). The Genesis record had said that not only man but also the earth was destroyed by the Flood (Genesis 6:13; 9:11). This destruction obviously did not mean *annihilation*, and therefore, must have meant some profound change in its surface and atmospheric features, its geography, hydrology, geology, meteorology, etc.

Since there was simultaneously taking place an unprecedented destruction of living creatures of all kinds, it is quite certain that hosts of these animals, and plants as well, must have been entrapped and buried in the resulting sediments, later to become lithified and preserved as vast "graveyards" of fossils. This conclusion is further verified by the Biblical record of the Edenic Curse. The original Creation was pronounced by God to be "very good," but when Adam sinned, God cursed the "ground" (earth) (Genesis 3:17; 5:29), thus introducing the principle of decay and death into the world. The plain implication of both this and the New Testament statements of Paul (Romans 5:12; 8:20-22; I Corinthians 15:21) is that death of sentient animal life, as well as human death, was non-existent in the world before the Curse.

Thus, fossil remains of once-living creatures — wherever found in the rocks of the earth — must have come from animals that died *after* man's fall. This can only mean that all fossiliferous deposits have been formed sometime within the span of human history. There seems, therefore, no better explanation for their existence in most cases than the Flood and its associated geological and hydraulic activities.

Consideration of the probable action of the flood waters and the sediments deposited by them leads to the conclusion that, at any given locality, the fossils deposited would tend to assume a certain peculiar order of superposition. That is, there would be a tendency for organisms of heavier specific weight, of simpler structure, of lower-elevation habitats, and of lesser capacity for swimming, running, or flying, to be entrapped earlier and buried deeper in the deluge sediments. More complex and active organisms, with upper-level habitats, would be buried later and higher, if at all. Many exceptions to these rules might be anticipated, because of the catastrophic nature of the Flood, but this would certainly be the general order, and this is of course exactly what is found in the earth's fossil-bearing sediments.

Instead of being acknowledged as evidence of the great Flood, however, these fossil deposits have instead been interpreted as demonstrating organic evolution! In fact, it is widely recognized by evolutionists that these fossil sequences supply the only apparent historical evidence that evolution has ever really occurred on more than a trivial scale. All other suggested evidences for

evolution — mutations, geographic distribution, anatomical resemblances, etc. — are strictly circumstantial in nature and can easily
be explained in terms of special creation and the general Biblical
framework of interpretation.

The importance of this conclusion becomes apparent when it
is realized that evolution has been taken as the scientific basis
and justification for practically all the anti-Christian systems of
these last days, including humanism, modernism, Freudianism,
Deweyism, socialism, and Communism, among others. These systems and philosophies are thus founded in large measure upon
a gross misinterpretation of the fossil record and its significance.
The evolutionary philosophy employs the so-called "principle of
uniformity," which assumes that *all things* in the present world
can be explained in terms of the uniform and continuous operation
of those natural laws and processes which can be studied and
measured in the present world. Supernatural or catastrophic in-
terventions by God into this "steady-state" universe, such as at
Creation or the Flood, are *a priori* rejected. The fossil record,
therefore, *must* be explained "scientifically," which means, by definition, in terms of uniformity and evolution.

But such explanations are, as we have seen, flatly contradicted
by the Biblical record of the Creation, the Curse, and the Deluge!
These events constitute such great discontinuities in the earth's
"natural processes" that any scientific conclusions based on uniformitarian principles as applied to these periods must necessarily
be invalid. On the other hand, if the Bible records of the Creation
and the Flood are inspired, reliable, lucid and meaningful —
as evangelical Christians certainly *ought* to believe them to be —
then full acceptance of their literal truth and perspicuity must
lead one eventually to a much more satisfactory correlation of all
the pertinent scientific data than evolutionary uniformitarianism
can ever provide.

Difficulties certainly exist in any such attempted reorientation
of the data of historical geology and related sciences. Space does
not allow discussion of such problems here, but certainly much
legitimate scientific evidence can be marshalled in support of
the Biblical viewpoint.

The modern significance of the Genesis Flood can hardly be
better stated than in the words of the apostle: "There shall come
in the last days scoffers, walking after their own lusts, And saying,
Where is the promise of His coming? for since the fathers fell
asleep, all things continue as they were from the beginning of
the Creation. For this they willingly are ignorant of, that by the
Word of God the heavens were of old, and the earth standing
out of the water and in the water: Whereby the world that then
was, being overflowed with water, perished" (II Peter 3:3-6).

XIV

SEVEN REASONS FOR OPPOSING EVOLUTION[1]

That the theory of evolution, as an all-embracing world view, is a philosophy of profound importance that *must* be reckoned with is becoming increasingly evident as its influence penetrates more and more deeply into every phase of modern life. Dr. Rene Dubos, in a national Sigma Xi Lecture Series, recently made the statement:

> Most enlightened persons now accept as a fact that everything in the cosmos — from heavenly bodies to human beings — has developed and continues to develop through evolutionary processes. The great religions of the West have come to accept a historical view of creation. Evolutionary concepts are applied also to social institutions and to the arts. Indeed, most political parties, as well as schools of theology, sociology, history, or arts, teach these concepts and make them the basis of their doctrine. Thus, theoretical biology now pervades all of Western culture indirectly through the concept of progressive historical change.[2]

Thus, evolution is not merely a biological theory, but is rather a full-blown cosmology. The whole structure of modern public education, from kindergarten through the postgraduate schools, both in content and methodology, is built around the evolutionary framework.

> Dewey's greatest importance in a theological interpretation of American history is to be found in the revolution which he brought about in the philosophy, purposes and methods of education. He applied his Instrumentalism to education in a remarkably consistent and thorough manner and, in so doing, he re-wrote American educational practice in the light of his evolutionary philosophy, largely derived from Darwin . . . the revolution in education became a powerful means for the furthering of the intellectual revolution which Darwin made possible.[3]

A Christian, therefore, simply cannot avoid confronting this issue of evolution. It now permeates every aspect of secular life,

---

[1]Reprinted from *Bibliotheca Sacra*, July-September, 1965. Vol. 122, No. 487, pp. 254-269.

[2]Rene Dubos. "Humanistic Biology," *American Scientist*, V. 53, March 1965, p. 6.

[3]C. Gregg Singer: *A Theological Interpretation of American History*, (Craig Press, Nutley, N. J., 1964) pp. 128-129.

and most areas of religious life as well. Small wonder that many professing Christians and the institutions with which they are associated (churches, schools, seminaries, publications, missions, etc.) have long since capitulated to evolution, and have tried to adapt their theology and Biblical exegesis to modern evolutionary science and social philosophy.

But a warning from the past is still in order. Nearly a hundred years ago the great theologian, Charles Hodge, after a closely-reasoned masterpiece of analysis concluded:

> We have thus arrived at the answer to our question, What is Darwinism? It is Atheism. This does not mean, as before said, that Mr. Darwin himself and all who adopt his views are atheists; but it means that his theory is atheistic.[4]

In this article, it is proposed to approach, in imagination, seven individuals, each representing a particular religious point of view, with the aim of demonstrating to him that the canons of his own system ought properly to preclude the evolutionary theory.

Biblical Christianity

Naturally, we contact first of all the Bible-believing Christian, since the reasons for opposing evolution are most clear-cut and obvious in his case. The Bible system involves a primeval Creation *ex nihilo*, perfect and complete, followed by an awful Fall into sin and the worldwide Curse of God, requiring intervention by God Himself, in Christ, to arrest and reverse the resulting age-long tragedy of deterioration and death. The wonderful provision of redemption and salvation, through the sacrificial grace of God in Christ, is available to the lost sinner freely, appropriated through faith apart from all works of human effort. The Creation itself shall also be redeemed from the bondage of corruption in that great Day ordained by its Creator and Redeemer.

Evolution, on the other hand, not only must deny Creation, but must also deny the Fall, and therefore also the necessity of redemption. Evolution is essentially development by innate processes out of prior materials, by chance and random variation, through the struggle for existence and natural selection, with ever higher and higher orders of organization and life developed over hundreds of millions of years. Finally, creatures are evolved whose brain-structure is so highly integrated that they are able to understand, and then to control, the processes of evolution. Thus,

---

[4]Charles Hodge, *What Is Darwinism?*, New York, Scribner, Armstrong & Co., 1874), p. 177.

by dint of ages of blind struggle and then perhaps by a few centuries of controlled effort and good works, life will come out into its ultimate state of perfection.

Thus, it is clear that evolution, at least in the form held by those who are the real leaders and authorities in evolutionary thought, is quite plainly in radical opposition to all the fundamental tenets of Biblical Christianity.

Old Testament Orthodoxy

There are many people, not necessarily Christians, who accept the Old Testament as of divine authority (Jews, Moslems, etc.). As we approach such a believer in the Old Testament, we do so in confidence, knowing that the volume of Scriptures in which he trusts unequivocally teaches the doctrine of special Creation. Its account of Creation, as centered especially in the first two chapters of Genesis, is unparalleled in majesty and beauty, describing as it does the creation *ex nihilo* of all things by God, and His forming them into their present order in six days. All other ancient cosmogonies are evolutionary in essence, beginning with pre-existent materials and allowing the "gods" or forces of nature to operate on them in some way to bring them into their present form. Thus, it is clear that the Biblical cosmogony could not have been borrowed from pagan sources nor could it have been written merely as an accommodation to the mentality of the early Hebrews, accustomed as were all early peoples to think more naturally in an evolutionary context.

The Creation account of Genesis is written in chronologic form, as sober history, with the work of each day successively described. Ten times the phrase "after its kind," is used, making it plain that individual variations in the basic kinds were always to be within certain limits, a restriction which definitely would preclude real evolution. Furthermore, the conclusion of the Creation period is marked by the heavily-emphasized statement that God "rested" from all His works which He "created and made." Thus, it is categorically stated that the processes of the Creation period, by which all things were brought into their present form, are no longer in operation (Genesis 2:1-3). This fact is again emphasized in the Ten Commandments (Exodus 20:11).

At the end of the six days, therefore, God's creative and formative acts had all been completed. The world was finished, and everything was "very good" (Genesis 1:31), with nothing out of harmony, no disorder, no decay and above all, no death. There was no struggle for existence, because God had provided ample food for every living thing. The Creation period had truly been one of development and organizing and progress, from the simple to the complex — water had been elevated above the earth, lands had been elevated above the seas, the inorganic materials of the earth's structure had been organized into living plant life, the primeval light energy had been organized into great light-bearers, the earth's water and chemical materials had been organized into animal bodies and imbued with the breath of lives, and man himself had been built up from the dust of the earth into the most highly organized system in the entire physical universe and then given not only the living soul shared by animals but also an eternal spirit — the very image of God!

But all this infinite amount of developing and organizing had been accomplished directly by the Creator Himself — not over billions of years, but in six days! There is no evidence in the context of the narrative for understanding the word *day* to have any meaning other than the ordinary literal meaning. In fact, to make this crystal clear, God defined the word when it was first introduced. "God called the light *Day*" (Genesis 1:5). The successive periods of light, therefore, as the earth turned on its axis, were the successive *days*, in which God made all things.

And since the Creation was *finished*, there has been nothing comparable going on in the world since that time. If one wishes to call the developmental processes of the six days "evolution," he must at least recognize that such processes have never been in existence since the terminus of that period. But such a position is impossible for the true evolutionist to accept, since he insists that all past history can be explained in terms of *present* processes, those which are susceptible of scientific study and understanding.

But there is more. The Genesis account records how, because of the entrance of spiritual disorder into the world when man sinned, God pronounced a curse on man's entire dominion (Genesis 3:17-19). Instead of processes of development and organization, the processes of the world became processes of increasing disorder and decay and death. Even the appointed king over the earth, man himself, whose body had been organized from the earth's elements, would now be bound by a continual process of decay and disorganization, finally returning to the same elements from which his body had come. Thus, the basic law of the world became, not a law of evolution, but a law of deterioration. The agelong existence of struggle, suffering, destruction and catastrophe, associated with the universal reign of sin and death, from which only God Himself can bring salvation, is plain and powerful evidence that evolution, in the present economy, is an utterly false doctrine.

New Testament Faith

Many people (we might call them "progressive revelationists") would say, however, that the Old Testament is no longer valid. Its outlook is prescientific, and its religious insights are couched in "mythological" forms. The New Testament, on the other hand, is now in effect and is thus the sole rule of faith and practice.

But such "New Testament Christians" should also see clearly that the theory of evolution is repudiated again and again in this part of the Bible. The writer of Hebrews, for example, stresses that all things were made out of nothing (not out of prior materials, as evolutionists must contend), by the Word of God (Hebrews 11:3). He also agrees with the writer of Genesis that all of God's creative activity ceased with the end of the Creation week (Hebrews 4:3, 10). The Apostle Paul writes that there actually are distinct "kinds" of creatures, as the Genesis account had said. "But God giveth it a body as it hath pleased him, and to every seed his own body. All flesh is not the same flesh; but there is one kind of flesh of men, another flesh of beasts, another of fishes, and another of birds" (I Corinthians 15:38, 39). The evolutionist, on the other hand, thinks in terms of a basic continuity of all kinds of living matter. As Dubos says:

> Comparative biology has revealed, furthermore, that man is linked to all living organisms through a common line of descent, and shares with them many characteristics of physicochemical constitution and of biological organization; the philosophical concept of the "great chain of being" can thus be restated now in the form of a scientific generalization.[5]

The universal rule of decay and death is prominent in New Testament theology. The Creation has been made "subject to futility," and is under the "bondage of decay," "groaning and travailing in pain together" (Romans 8:20-22). The earth and its atmospheric heavens are "waxing old like a garment," and shall be "folded up," and "perish" (Hebrews 1:11, 12). Not only the physical universe, but also "all flesh is like grass," which "withereth" (I Peter 1:24).

As a matter of fact, it is quite inconsistent for anyone to claim allegiance to the New Testament unless he also accepts the Old Testament, since the writers of the former clearly believed in the divine inspiration and full historical accuracy of the Old Testament. Frequent references are made to the narrative of Genesis 1-3, always with evident complete reliance in its historicity (Luke 3:38; Romans 5:12-19; I Corinthians 11:8, 9; 15:21, 22; 15:45-47; II Corinthians 11:3; I Timothy 2:13-15; I Peter 3:5;

---

[5]Rene Dubos, *op. cit.*, p. x.

for example). Even Jesus Christ Himself quoted from the Creation account, quoting both Genesis 1:27 and 2:24 in the same statement (Matthew 19:4, 5; Mark 10:6, 7). The great doctrines of Creation, the Fall, the Curse, and the promised Saviour, which have their true foundation in the first chapters of Genesis, and which are so completely contradicted by the evolutionary philosophy, are also the major doctrines of the New Testament.

Religious Liberalism

But now we pass on to the man who is bound by neither the Old nor the New Testament. He insists that he is religious, however, believing in God and in spiritual and moral values. He does admire certain parts of the Bible, such as the Sermon on the Mount, the golden rule, the "love" principle, etc. He accepts the ethics of Christianity, but not its dogmatics. He desires to advance the cause of human brotherhood and love, and believes in the universal fatherhood of God.

Now if such a religious liberal were truly consistent in his thinking, he would have to recognize that evolutionary ethics are diametrically opposed to the Christian ethics he espouses. The very genius of evolution is natural selection, the process by which the fittest survive and the unfit are destroyed. For true evolutionary progress, therefore, the principle of self-interest for the individual and the group of which he is a part must be paramount. An artificial preservation of the unfit can be nothing but deleterious to future evolution. "Self-preservation is the first law of nature."

But this is not the Christian ethic! Why, in the very Sermon on the Mount, so esteemed by the liberals, Christ said: "Blessed are the meek, blessed are the merciful, blessed are the poor in spirit, blessed are the peacemakers" (Matthew 5:3-9). Such a policy is surely subversive of natural selection. Christ, in the same sermon, refuted the concept of the struggle for existence: "Ye have heard that it hath been said, An eye for an eye, and a tooth for a tooth: but I say unto you, That ye resist not evil: but whosoever shall smite thee on thy right cheek, turn to him the other also" (Matthew 5:38, 39). "Love your enemies, bless them that curse you, do good to them that hate you, and pray for them which despitefully use you, and persecute you" (Matthew 5:44).

The chief good in the evolutionary process is survival, since only that which survives can possibly contribute to further evolution. But Jesus said: "Whosoever will save his life shall lose it" (Matthew 16:25). Thus, the ethics of evolution are those of struggle and survival. Christian ethics, on the other hand, center in self-sacrifice and love.

Theism

Next in line we approach the man who gives no allegiance to Christianity or to its Scriptures at all, and perhaps not to any other formal religious system. But he does believe in God; he is not an atheist. He sees so much evidence of design and order that he agrees there must have been a First Cause, and that there must be, therefore, some kind of meaning to life and some kind of purpose in the universe.

If such is really his belief, then of course he ought to reject evolution out of hand, since evolution is completely random and purposeless, at least according to its leaders. As George Gaylord Simpson, probably the nation's leading paleontologist, has repeatedly said in these or similar words:

> The fossil record shows very clearly that there is no central line leading steadily, in a goal-directed way, from a protozoan to man. Instead there has been continual and extremely intricate branching, and whatever course we follow through the branches there are repeated changes both in the rate and in the direction of evolution. Man is one ultimate twig. The housefly, the dog flea, the apple tree, and millions of other kinds of organisms are similarly the ends of others. Moreover, we do not find that life has simply expanded, branching into increasing diversity, until the organisms now living had evolved. On the contrary, the vast majority of earlier forms of life have become extinct without issue.[6]

The evolutionary process thus seems to manifest no order and no purpose, but to be quite random. The genetic mutations which nourish it are random in their occurrence and thus nearly always deleterious in their effects.

Now, if evolutionary mechanics can satisfactorily explain the origin of all things, and if evolutionary history gives no evidence of order and purpose, what ground is there for postulating a personal, purposive Creator as the Cause of all this? God becomes an unnecessary hypothesis. And, especially, if man was to be the goal of evolution, what possible sense can be made out of billions of years of random variation, struggle, suffering, death, wholesale extinctions of dinosaurs and other animals who died out before man arrived, and all the rest of the evolutionary history? Thus, a real understanding of evolution precludes simultaneous belief in God.

[6]George Gaylord Simpson. "The Nonprevalence of Humanoids," *Science*, Volume 143, p. 773, February 21, 1964.

Ethical Humanism

To a great many intellectuals today the concept of a personal God is thus considered unscientific and unnecessary, forever displaced by the grander idea of evolution. We now come to an individual of this persuasion. Although he may deny God as a person, he may yet be quite a religious individual, with an impassioned desire to elevate mankind and to improve society. He may even believe in some kind of cosmic force which he calls God, but in a pantheistic sense. He is a humanist, and since he harbors noble ideals and strives to transform society in accord with those ideals, we could call him an ethical, or altruistic, humanist.

If such a man is truly sincere, as we should at least assume, then any philosophy which breeds hate and destruction among men should be utterly repudiated by him. On this basis alone, the ethical humanist should recognize that evolution must be false doctrine. With its continual emphasis on struggle and self-interest, on changing regimes of nature, on survival of the fittest, and similar ideas, it has naturally been taken as the scientific foundation of every social philosophy which seeks to pit class against class, or nation against nation, or race against race.

Evolution is found at the base of the destructive militarism of the past century, of facism and Naziism and of all forms of socialism and anarchism. Most importantly, in the present world context, it is very definitely and directly connected with communism. As Jaques Barzun, a prominent contémporary historian, Dean of the Graduate Faculties at Columbia University, has said:

> It is a commonplace that Marx felt his own work to be the exact parallel of Darwin's. He even wished to dedicate a portion of *Das Kapital* to the author of *The Origin of Species*.[7]

It is no mere coincidence that modern communist dogma is squarely structured around evolution, both in biologic history and in economic history. The utter disregard of truth and the moral law generally, the hatred for God and religion, the savage destruction of human life when the opportunity affords, and other such characteristics of communism in practice, all fit perfectly into the evolutionary scheme, that process which supposedly impels mankind inexorably onward to the next evolutionary stage.

> There was truth in Engels' eulogy on Marx: "Just as Darwin discovered the law of evolution in organic nature, so Marx discovered the law of evolution in human history." What they both celebrated was

---

[7]Jacques Barzun. *Darwin, Marx, Wagner*, (2nd. Ed., New York, Doubleday, 1958), p. 8.

the internal rhythm and course of life, the one the life of nature, the other of society, that proceeded by fixed laws, undistracted by the will of God or men. There were no inexplicable acts, no violations of the natural order. God was as powerless as individual men to interfere with the internal, self-adjusting dialectic of change and development.[8]

Not only is evolution the basis of social Darwinism and all its evil progeny — fascism as well as communism, laissez-faire capitalism as well as militaristic imperialism — it is also at the root of most of the baleful educational and psychological theories which have opened Pandora's box in these latter days.

The supposed animal kinship of man is the rationale for much of the modern psychological experimentation with animals. The behavior of animals supposedly provides clues to the basic desires and frustrations of men. If men really are animals, then it is physiologically healthy for them to act like animals, so the reasoning would go. This presupposition is intrinsic in Freudianism, behaviorism, Kinseyism. This is behind the permissiveness of the progressive educationism which has captured the public schools, especially since the days of John Dewey.

> "Dewey's conviction that there was no truth, but only a 'warranted assertibility' had many dangerous implications which were not always apparent to some of his faithful and enthuiastic devotees who took progressive education theory and practice to every corner of the nation. This educational philosophy was, as Dewey himself conceded, anti-Christian. It struck at the very heart of Christian principles. The psychology on which it was based denied that man had a soul but taught that he was just an animal, but higher in intelligence than other animals."[9]

The modern fruit of two generations of Freudianism and Deweyism is seen in the almost universal animal amoralism which has permeated our once-Christian culture. Surely, whether or not a man even believes in a personal God, he should be able to see quite clearly that the evolutionary philosophy has brought nothing but degradation to mankind as a whole. The altruistic humanist, concerned as he is for the betterment of mankind and society, should certainly reject evolution.

Scientific Rationalism

Finally, we come to the scientist, the man whose religion, if it be called such, is merely the pursuit of truth. He is not concerned with

---

[8]Gertrude Himmelfarb: *Darwin and the Darwinian Revolution* (London, Chatto & Windus, 1959), p. 348.
[9]C. Gregg Singer, *op cit.*, p. 130.

metaphysics or mysticism in any form. It is his business simply to measure and understand things as they are. He is a pragmatist, and accepts as fact only that which he can prove or observe experimentally.

Of all people, there is perhaps less reason for the scientist, than for any other, to accept evolution. By its very nature, evolutionary history is beyond the reach of his scientific method, having to do with origins, with events of the pre-historic past which are non-repeatable and nonmeasurable.

Furthermore, it is quite impossible to extrapolate from the processes of the present world, which are available for scientific measurement, into the past far enough to determine the real facts of the origins and development of all things. This is clear from the simple fact that the processes of the present world are not in any sense processes of origins and development, but rather of conservation and decay.

This is a profoundly important truth which needs to be recognized and emphasized on a far larger scale than it has been heretofore. All of the various *processes* of the universe — whether physical, biological, geological, chemical, or of any other field of science — must operate within the framework of just two basic *laws*. These are the first and second laws of thermodynamics, the laws of energy conservation and deterioration. They define the state of the measurable universe as one of quantitative stability and qualitative decay. Nothing is now being either created or destroyed, but that which presently exists is becoming less ordered and less useful, drifting down toward an ultimate condition of quiescence and death.

Every type of process in the universe involves interchanges of energy. The study of these processes, the delineating of their characteristics and the measurement of their rates of activity — this is precisely the domain of science. In a very real sense, therefore, science is simply the study of energy and its transformations from one kind into another. Even matter is a form of energy, so that actually everything in the observable universe is energy! And always, no matter what the particular process may be, it operates within the framework of the first and second laws of thermodynamics. There is no known exception to this generalization.

And these two laws are fundamentally and basically in opposition to the entire philosophy of evolution. Evolution says that present processes are the same as those by which the universe came into existence and is thus still coming into existence. But the first law of thermodynamics says that no energy (and this includes everything) is now coming into existence. No energy is being either created or destroyed.

Furthermore, evolution says that there is a universal law whereby things tend to become progressively more organized and more complex. The non-living becomes life; elementary particles become atoms and atoms become molecules; simple life forms develop into complex animals; beasts evolve into men. Note again the sweeping claims made for evolution by Dubos cited at the beginning of this article.

But the second law of thermodynamics says that there is a universal law operating throughout the observable universe whereby everything tends to become less organized, to become disordered, to decay and die.

> Man has long been aware that his world has a tendency to fall apart. Tools wear out, fishing nets need repair, roofs leak, iron rusts, wood decays, loved ones sicken and die, relatives quarrel, and nations make war. . . . We instinctively resent the decay of orderly system such as the living organism and work to restore such systems to their former or even higher levels of organization.[10]

In a scientific sense, all of this progress toward decay results from the fact that, in the energy exchanges comprising the particular process, some of the energy is converted into heat energy which cannot be recovered and reconverted into other forms. Thus, the universe as a whole, at least in so far as science can measure it, is proceeding inexorably to an ultimate "heat death," in which no more energy conversions, and thus no more useful work, will be possible. There is thus a universal law of change in the world, as the evolutionist contends, but this is a change downward, not upward. The principle of evolution is precisely the converse of the second law of thermodynamics, and therefore both cannot simultaneously be true. Locally and temporarily, there may be an excess inflow of ordering energy into a particular system, so that there appears to be growth and development for a while, but invariably this is only local and temporary and the decay principle wins out in the end.

The various evidences of change that are cited in favor of evolution — the processes of variation, selection, hybridization, mutation, and the like — actually conform perfectly to the two laws of thermodynamics. They represent either the out-working of inwrought mechanisms of genetic variability and adjustment to environment within the basic created kind or else, in the case of true mutations, a sudden, random change in the genetic structure which almost invariably must result in a decrease of organization and viability.

Thus, true science does not prove evolution at all, as often claimed, but rather disproves it. Science deals only with present processes, and present processes are not processes of origination

[10]Van Rensselaer Potter: "Society and Science," *Science*, Volume 146, p. 1018, Oct. 20, 1964.

and integration but rather of conservation and disintegration. Evolution in the true philosophical sense is not taking place at all in the present economy of nature, and that which may or may not have taken place in the prehistoric past is not within the domain of science. The true scientist, if he is really true to his scientific ideals, ought therefore certainly to reject the idea of evolution.

Two Reasons for Accepting Evolution

It has been shown in the foregoing that there are seven reasons, or, better, seven families of reasons, all of them legitimate and powerful reasons, why men of practically every variety of religious opinion should deny and oppose evolution. But if this is so, then it does seem passing strange that great numbers of men *accept* evolution. This is especially true among intellectuals, and others who are men of education and ability. Not only scientists and humanists, but also religious liberals and even some who profess faith in Biblical Christianity, have accepted evolution as a fact of history and even as basic in their cosmology. There must, therefore, be strong reasons for accepting evolution, in spite of the evidence listed above against it.

These reasons are not basically scientific in nature. As we have just seen, the basic structure of real scientific law is conservative and degradational, not evolutionary. The commonly cited evidences — comparative anatomy, comparative embryology, mutations, etc. — can all be understood better in the context of real Creation, with common basic plans used for similar functions by a common Designer, but with allowance for limited variation and adjustment to environmental changes. Even the fossil record, which is the only quasi-historical evidence offered in support of evolution, has essentially the same great gaps between major kinds of creatures as are found in the present world. Furthermore, the fossil record can be interpreted in various ways. The uniformitarian interpretation, which leads to the evolutionary framework, is no more able to explain the actual data than is the catastrophic interpretation.

Thus, evolution is certainly not "proved" by science, vociferous proponents thereof to the contrary notwithstanding. The real reasons for accepting evolution are not scientific, but religious, reasons!

There seem to be just two basic reasons. The first is that which motivates the real leaders of evolutionary thought. Evolution, with its implications of innate principles of progress and development, of self-interest and self-improvement, with man himself as the highest system yet evolved in the universe, now able to control future evolution through control of the social order and his own biological activities, is to such men an impelling religious idea. Furthermore, it frees them from responsibility to a sovereign God and Creator, to whom they might otherwise have to give a personal accounting at some future judgment day. Man becomes his own god, responsible only to himself or, more practically, to the intellectual elite who will become his spokesmen. This is the thought-world of men like Julian Huxley, H. J. Muller, George Gaylord Simpson, Oscar Riddle, Harlow Shapley, J. B. S. Haldane, even Father Pierre Teilhard de Chardin, and most of the rest of the world's leaders in the realm of evolutionary philosophy.

These are the modern-day counterparts of those men of old of whom the Scriptures speak, when they say:

> Professing themselves to be wise, they became fools, and changed the glory of the uncorruptible God into an image made like to corruptible man, and to birds, and fourfooted beasts, and creeping things. . . . Who changed the truth of God into a lie, and worshipped and served the creature more than the Creator. . . . Even as they did not like to retain God in their knowledge (Romans 1:22, 23, 25, 28).

Perhaps they are among the very men of whom Peter spoke prophetically, when he said:

> There shall come in the last days scoffers, walking after their own lusts, and saying, Where is the promise of his coming? for since the fathers fell asleep, all things continue as they were from the beginning of the Creation (II Peter 3:3, 4).

Many evolutionists are such because of just this reason. They do not like to retain God in their knowledge, and they abhor the thought of His coming one day to judge them. And if God is going to be ignored or rejected, then the only possible way in which the existence of the universe and its inhabitants can be explained is in terms of evolution. Evolution is an absolute necessity for anyone who would dethrone God. In the last analysis, therefore, the evolutionary philosophy must have its origin and rationale in the rebellion of Satan himself, who is engaged in an agelong war against God, seeking to usurp His place as King of the universe.

But most evolutionists are not committed in *this* way to the evolutionary system. Undoubtedly a great many people sincerely believe in both God and in evolution. They are not against God, and some of them even say they believe in both evolution and the divine inspiration of the Bible — although, as we have seen, this is an utterly contradictory position.

Most people believe in evolution because — most people believe in evolution! They are evolutionists because they are conformists. The great pressure that has developed through the influence of the first group of evolutionists, as described above, has been tremendously successful in persuading people that, in order to be "scientific," they simply must accept evolution as a fact, whether they like it or not. Most people who believe in evolution, no matter how much education they may have, will be found to have only the most nebulous understanding of the real evidences for and against evolution; similarly most people have even less understanding of the tremendous weight of evidence supporting the inspired accuracy of the Holy Scriptures, and their clear teaching of special Creation.

They have not studied the issue for themselves, but have simply been pressured into believing it. They will not "study to show themselves approved unto God" (II Timothy 2:15). They "love the praise of men more than the praise of God" (John 12:43). They prefer to be "conformed to this world" (Romans 12:2).

As Elijah once said to the people of God:

How long halt ye between two opinions? If Baal be God, follow him, but if the Lord be God, follow Him (I Kings 18:21).

A man cannot be *truly* Christian or altruistic, or even scientific, and also believe in evolution.

XV

SCIENCE VERSUS SCIENTISM IN HISTORICAL GEOLOGY[1]

The study of historical geology holds great fascination for many people who are neither historians nor geologists. This discipline occupies a uniquely interesting and important position in human thought. Among the humanities, the study of history surely is of singular significance and, among the sciences, geology, dealing as it does with the very earth itself, is similarly of unique interest. When the two are combined in historical geology, which professes to be able to decipher the mystery of the origin and history of the earth and its processes, the resulting panorama is of marvelous interest and significance. Such a picture, in fact, is of far more than historical and geological pertinence. Anything which elucidates origins is necessarily of philosophical and theological interest, with strong implications regarding meanings and purposes and destinies as well.

It is little wonder, then, that historical geology has attracted the intense interest and concern of a great variety of people. As a matter of fact, the basic structure of modern historical geology was worked out over a hundred years ago by such men as James Hutton (an agriculturalist with medical training), John Playfair (a mathematician), William Smith (a surveyor), Charles Lyell (a lawyer), Georges Cuvier (a comparative anatomist), Charles Darwin (an apostate divinity student and naturalist), Robert Chambers (a journalist), William Buckland (a theologian), Roderick Murchison (a soldier and gentleman of leisure), Adam Sedgwick (who, when seeking election to the chair of geology at Cambridge, boasted that he knew nothing of geology), Hugh Miller (a stonesmason), John Fleming (a zoologist), and others of like assortment.

Although the basic framework of historical geology, as worked out by these men, has not changed to the present day, there has arisen a group of specialists in historical geology who have come to regard this field as their own particular field of *science*, and who now regard with some disdain any who venture to write or speak

---

[1]This paper was first presented at a Conference on "Creation, Darwinism and Christian Schools," sponsored by the Association for Christian Schools at the St. Thomas Episcopal Church in Houston, Texas, May 1965, and published in the Proceedings of that Conference. It has also been published in the Quarterly of the Creation Research Society, Vol. 2, October 1965.

in this field without giving full allegiance to the accepted system. By its very nature, however, historical geology is not, and can never be, a genuine *science,* and therefore the dogmatic insistence that one follow the interpretations of its founders and present-day leaders, with all the implications of origins and meanings that are involved, is nothing less than *scientism.*

This is in no way meant to be a reflection upon the science of geology, which is a true science in every sense of the word, and which has made a tremendous contribution to our understanding and application of the laws of nature. When, however, a geologist (or lawyer or surveyor or naturalist or anyone else) seeks to become a *historical* geologist, he must leave the realm of science and enter that of philosophy or religion. The presently accepted system of historical geology is basically nothing else than a philosophy or a religion of evolutionary uniformitarianism. If this fact were only recognized and acknowledged by its adherents, no one would be greatly disturbed but, when this system is widely promulgated and insisted upon in the name of *science,* it has degenerated into mere scientism instead. This will become more evident as we consider the true meaning of science and the true nature of those physical processes studied by science.

What Is Science?

The word "science" itself of course is derived from the Latin *scientia* ("knowledge"), and this is essentially what it means. A more formal definition, as given in the Oxford dictionary is:

A branch of study which is concerned either with a connected body of demonstrated truths or with observed facts systematically classified and more or less colligated by being brought under general laws, and which includes trustworthy methods for the discovery of new truth within its own domain.

Science thus involves facts which are observed and laws which have been demonstrated. The scientific method involves experimental reproducibility, with like causes producing like effects. It is *knowledge,* not inference or speculation or extrapolation.

True science thus is necessarily limited to the measurement and study of *present* phenomena and processes. Data which have been actually observed in the present, or which have been recorded by human observers in the historic past, are properly called scientific data. Laws which have been deduced from these data, which satisfactorily correlate the pertinent data and which have predictive value for the correlation of similar data obtained from like experiments in the future, are properly regarded as scientific laws.

But there is obviously no way of knowing that these processes and the laws which describe them have always been the same in the past or that they will always be the same in the future. It is possible to make an assumption of this kind, of course, and this is the well-known principle of *uniformitarianism*. The assumption is reasonable, in the light of our experience with present processes, and it is no doubt safe to extrapolate on this basis for a certain time into the future and back into the past. But to insist that uniformitarianism is the only scientific approach to the understanding of *all* past and future time is clearly nothing but a dogmatic tenet of a particular form of religion.

That uniformitarianism has been the foundational and guiding principle of historical geology is widely recognized. A standard textbook on the subject says, for example:

> The uprooting of such fantastic beliefs [that is, those of the catastrophists —*author*] began with the Scottish geologist, James Hutton, whose *Theory of the Earth*, published in 1785, maintained that *the present is the key to the past*, and that, given sufficient time, processes now at work could account for all the geologic features of the Globe. This philosophy, which came to be known as the *doctrine of uniformitarianism* demands an immensity of time; it has now gained universal acceptance among intelligent and informed people.[2]

Thus, science deals with the data and processes of the present, which can be experimentally measured and observationally verified. The principle of uniformity is a philosophy, or faith, by which it is hoped that these processes of the present can be extrapolated into the distant past and the distant future to explain all that has ever happened and to predict all that will ever happen.

But, when viewed in these terms, it is obvious that uniformity is not proved, and therefore is not properly included in the definition of science. There may be any number of other assumptions which might serve as the basis of such extrapolation, and all would similarly be mere acts of faith.

It is perfectly possible and reasonable, as we shall see, to assume that the processes studied by science were themselves created at some time in the past and will be terminated at some time in the future. The processes themselves then could tell us nothing about their creation or termination — this would be outside the domain of scientific investigation. Such information could come, if at all, only by revelation from their Creator.

As a matter of fact, a full and complete understanding of any process, even in its present character, could in that case be obtained only in the context and framework of the fact of its prior creation.

[2]Carl O. Dunbar: *Historical Geology,"* (2nd. Ed., John Wiley and Sons, New York, 1960), p. 18. Emphasis is his.

This is because *meaning* is inextricably inter-related with *origin* and *destiny*.

Apart from this stricture, however, it is possible and proper to study science, in the sense of present processes, without reference to the past or future. Thus, the science of physics deals with the present processes of the physical world; the science of chemistry deals with the present chemical properties and behaviour of matter; the science of geology deals with present geological processes and earth features; the science of biology deals with the processes of life in plants, animals and man. So long as the question of *origins* or *ends* is not considered, there will be no conflict between the Bible and science. The Bible has numerous references to present phenomena of science, and all will be found in strict accord with the actual observed data. It is only when questions of origins or destinies (or fundamental meanings) are considered that conflicts appear.

To a considerable degree, therefore, a *Christian* study of physics or chemistry or other science can proceed along the same lines as a treatment by non-Christians. The same textbooks can be used, the same experimental apparatus, the same methods, provided only that the study is limited to an elucidation of the actual present properties and processes of the data of that science. But as soon as intrinsic meanings or origins or destinies are brought into the treatment, there will inevitably be conflict between the uniformitarian and Christian world-views.

The Processes of Science

Assuming that our study of science will be, as is proper, limited to the study of present processes, we soon encounter a most remarkable and significant fact. Regardless of the particular discipline of science we study — physics, chemistry, biology, geology, etc. — these processes all are built upon two basic concepts and follow two basic laws. The two basic concepts are *energy* and *entropy*, and the two laws are the *first and second laws of thermodynamics*.

Since the implications of these laws are highly important to the Christian cosmology, it will be well to allow a non-theist, thoroughly evolutionary and uniformitarian in his philosophy, to define them. Dr. Harold F. Blum, the Princeton biologist, states them as follows:

> Energy appears in various forms: heat, light, kinetic energy, mechanical work, chemical energy, and so forth. Energy can change its form but not its quantity — this is a statement of the *first law of thermodynamics*, which until quite recently could be accepted without qualification. We know, now, that matter is another form of energy, but

154 Studies in THE BIBLE AND SCIENCE

that does not alter this fundamental principle which is also called the law of conservation of energy.[3]

Energy is the concept which measures the capacity of doing work. Thus, everything in the physical universe, including matter and all the phenomena associated with matter, is essentially one or another form of energy. This first law of thermodynamics, which was proved empirically about a century ago, is really the most basic of all scientific laws. It has been verified in countless thousands of experiments, ranging from those on the scale of the sub-nuclear particles to measurements of the stars and galaxies, and there is no known exception. Thus, according to this most basic and best-proved of all scientific laws, there is *nothing which is now being created or destroyed*. Present processes, with which alone true science is able to deal, are *not* processes of creation.

With respect to the second law, Blum continues:

> The *second law of thermodynamics* cannot be put in such concise form as the first; it is stated in numerous ways, according to the kind of problem under study. . . . It is one of this law's consequences that all real processes go irreversibly. Let us consider a universe in which the total amount of energy remains, supposedly, constant. Any given process in this universe is accompanied by a change in magnitude of a quantity called the *entropy*. . . . All real processes go with an increase of entropy. The entropy also measures the randomness or lack of orderliness of the system, the greater the randomness the greater the entropy; . . .[4]

Thus, the second law of thermodynamics states that there is a universal tendency toward disorder and decay. In any finite open system, of course, there may be temporarily and locally an increase of order, due to the influx of ordering energy from outside the system, but the tendency is always ultimately downward toward disintegration and. death. This law also is proved beyond question, with no known exceptions. As Blum says, in the preface to the third edition of his book:

> Wishful thinking to the contrary, the second law of thermodynamics remains with us; . . . no wise scientist will, I think, deny its existence or import.[5]

Since we are here specially concerned with geological processes, the testimony of a prominent geologist will also be cited. Dr. Brian Mason, who is Curator of Physical Geology and Mineralogy at the American Museum of Natural History, says:

> In redistribution and recombination of the chemical elements in min-

---

[3]Harold F. Blum: *Time's Arrow and Evolution* (Torchbook Edition, New York, Harper and Brothers, 1962), p. 14.
[4]*Ibid.*, pp. 14, 15.
[5]*Ibid.*, p. v.

erals and rocks the atoms or ions lose part of their energy and yield more stable systems. Every rock exemplifies the laws conditioning the stability of crystal lattices, laws which follow the general principles of the structure of matter and of thermodynamics . . . the study of equilibria in laboratory experiments and by thermodynamic methods has thrown a flood of light on geochemical reactions, such as the origin of rocks and minerals, the processes of weathering and decomposition, and other kinds of transformations going on within the earth. . . . The major value of thermodynamics in geochemistry is that it provides a general approach to problems of stability, equilibrium, and chemical change.[6]

Thus, the two laws of thermodynamics are not simply laws of physics and engineering, as they are too often considered to be, but are universal laws governing the behaviour of all matter and processes on the earth, including those of biology, as Blum has shown, and of geology, as Mason has shown. The first law teaches that energy (which includes everything in the physical universe) is quantitatively constant. The second law teaches that energy is qualitatively deteriorating. Thus, *the present processes of nature are not processes of creation and integration, but rather of conservation and disintegration.*

All real processes in the universe therefore involve change, which means essentially exchanges of energy, or transformations of energy from one kind into another. But these changes are basically processes of decay. Locally and temporarily there may be processes which seem to be processes of growth and integration (such as the growth of a child or the growth of a crystal or the manufacture of an automobile). But these are due to a temporary excess influx of ordering energy into the system. Eventually, though, the child will grow old and die, the crystal will disintegrate, and the automobile will end up in the auto graveyard. Most processes fail even to exhibit this tentative growth character. In geology, for example, the typical processes are those of erosion, heat flow, radioactive decay, etc. In fact, it is such processes as these whose measured rates have served as the basis for geochronological calculations. But here a very important caution is in order. Although the second law of thermodynamics indicates that any system must decay, it says nothing about the rate of decay. As Mason says:

It is important to realize, however, that thermodynamics cannot predict the *rate* at which a reaction will proceed and does not tell us anything of the mechanism of the reaction.[7]

---

[6]Brian Mason: *Principles of Geochemistry* (2nd. Ed., New York, John Wiley & Sons, Inc., 1960), pp. 64, 68.

[7]*Ibid.*, p. 68.

And, similarly, Blum says:

> The second law of thermodynamics points the direction of events in time, but does not tell when or how fast they will go.[8]

These rates of decay will depend upon many variables, and in nearly all cases must be determined empirically, by actual measurements. There is never any assurance that the decay rates will be constant, as they may well change if the factors which influence them change. All geochronometers are suspect from this cause alone.

The True Uniformitarianism

We can now see that the concept of uniformitarianism, while perfectly valid and proper in its legitimate framework, has been applied quite illegitimately in historical geology. True uniformity has to do with the inviolability of natural *law* (e.g., the laws of thermodynamics), and not with the uniformity of process *rates*. The laws of thermodynamics indicate what the character of all natural processes must be, but they do not indicate how fast or how slow such processes will proceed. And there is certainly never any assurance that the rate of any given process will always be constant.

But it is this assumed uniformity of process rates which is at the very hub of the principle of uniformity as it has been applied in historical geology. This is evident from the following rather typical description of the principle:

> Opposed to this line of thinking was Sir Charles Lyell (1797-1875), a contemporary of Cuvier, who held that earth changes were gradual, taking place at the same uniform slowness that they are today. Lyell is thus credited with the propagation of the premise that more or less has guided geological thought ever since, namely that *the present is the key to the past*. In essence, Lyell's *doctrine of uniformitarianism* stated that past geological processes operated in the same manner and at the same rate they do today.[9]

Now it is quite obvious that if geological processes have always been going on at the same slow rates they exhibit today, the earth must be immensely old. Age calculations by certain of these processes — such as radioactive decay, continental erosion, canyon-cutting, deltaic deposition, oceanic sodium increments, when based on present rates, are of course bound to give extremely high values,

---

[8]Blum, *op cit.*, p. 16.
[9]James H. Zumberge: *Elements of Geology* (2nd. Ed., New York, John Wiley and Sons, Inc., 1963), p. 200. Emphasis is his.

far greater than can possibly be accommodated within the framework of Biblical chronology.

But there is clearly no scientific basis for assuming such uniformity of process rates. It is quite valid to assume that running water will erode soil and rock, that radioactive minerals will decay, and that all other such processes will proceed irreversibly, in accord with the second law of thermodynamics, but neither this nor any other scientific law provides any guarantee that such rates will always be slow and uniform. In fact, it is certain that all such real decay processes are so intricately complex and are affected by such a great number of factors (a change in any one of which may drastically affect the process rate) that it will forever be quite impossible to say exactly what the rate will be except under very precisely known and experimentally confirmed conditions.

It is encouraging that many geologists in recent years are beginning to recognize and acknowledge this distinction. For example, Zumberge, in a widely used introductory text, after defining uniformitarianism as above, cautions:

> From a purely scientific point of view, it is unwise to accept uniformitarianism as unalterable dogma. As pointed out in chapter one, man's experience with geological processes is restricted to only a minute fraction of the total span of earth history. He should never close his mind to the possibility that conditions in past geological time were different than today, and that the doctrine of uniformitarianism may not apply in every case where the reconstruction of some segment of earth history is involved.[10]

A very strong statement of the pitfalls of uniformitarianism in attempting to explain the sedimentary rocks is given by a member of the geology faculty at Pennsylvania State University:

> Conventional uniformitarianism, or "gradualism," i.e., the doctrine of unchanging change, is verily contradicted by all post-Cambrian sedimentary data and the geotectonic histories of which these sediments are the record. Thus, quantitative interpretations of the Ordovician from the Recent are meaningless.[11]

More recently, a Columbia University geologist has clearly tried to distinguish between the true and the fallacious uniformitarianism (calling them methodological and substantive uniformitatianism, respectively):

> Uniformitarianism is a dual concept. Substantive uniformitarianism (a testable theory of geologic change postulating uniformity of rates or material conditions) is false and stifling to hypothesis formation.

---

[10]*Ibid.*, p. 201.
[11]P. D. Krynine: "Uniformitarianism Is A Dangerous Doctrine," *Journal of Paleontology*, Volume 30, 1956, p. 1004.

Methodological uniformitarianism (a procedural principle asserting spatial and temporal invariance of natural laws) belongs to the definition of science and is not unique to geology.[12]

With this we would heartily agree. Uniformity of natural laws is basic in science, and is quite in accord with Scripture (always allowing, of course, for the possible miraculous interruption of those laws by the Creator when He so wills). But the type of geological uniformitarianism which has held sway for a hundred years, and which has indeed served as the very foundation of the theory of evolution, is not only contrary to the Biblical record, but is completely inadequate to explain the actual data of geology.

Substantive uniformitarianism as a descriptive theory has not withstood the test of new data and can no longer be maintained in any strict manner.[13]

Since geological uniformitarianism in the traditional sense can no longer be maintained, and since uniformitarianism in the true sense is in no way a peculiar possession of the science of geology, it is thus completely wrong to refer to uniformitarianism as being in some way particularly the possession of geological theory. An illuminating admission giving the reason why this identification continues to be made is revealed in the following:

As a special term, methodological uniformitarianism was useful only when science was debating the status of the supernatural in its realm; for if God intervenes, then laws are not invariant and induction becomes invalid. . . . The term today is an anachronism for we need no longer take special pains to affirm the scientific nature of our discipline.[14]

If one looks beneath the surface of these reasonings, he begins to see that the real problem is not one of science at all, but of scientism! That is, historical geologists have attempted to defend substantive uniformitarianism (i.e., uniformity of process rates) by citing the undisputed evidences of methodological uniformitarianism (i.e., uniformity of natural law). Whether this fallacy in reasoning has been conscious or sub-conscious is really immaterial; the basic reason for it in either case, has been the innate desire to relegate the position of the Creator and His possible intervention in history as far back in time as possible, and perhaps even to eliminate Him altogether. A full-orbed philosophy — nay, a religion — of origins and development has thus been erected upon a fallacious uniformitarianism. And this is scientism, not science.

---

[12]Stephen Jay Gould: "Is Uniformitarianism Necessary?" *American Journal of Science,* Volume 263, March 1965, p. 223.

[13]*Ibid.,* p. 226.

[14]*Ibid.,* p. 227.

The Evolutionary Framework

The vast ages of earth history which supposedly are implied by the principle of uniformity have been subdivided into a more or less standard series of geological eras and periods, each with a generally accepted name and approximate duration. The whole sequence is known as the Geological Column, and the corresponding chronology is known as the Geological Time Scale. This of course is the very backbone of the so-called historical geology. Any given rock formation must occupy a certain position in the Column, and presumably it can be dated as to time of formation in terms of the Time Scale.

A highly pertinent question needs asking at this point. On what basis are the various rock types and formations identified and classified? How is one system assigned to, say, the Devonian Period and another to the Ordovician? How do we know which is older and which is younger? How are the divisions between successive periods recognized?

As a matter of fact, this problem of stratigraphic classification is involved in no little uncertainty and controversy at the present time, even though the Geologic Time Scale has been generally accepted in its present form for about a hundred years.

The layman is inclined to assume that the principle of superposition is the main factor in determining relative age, and that equivalent strata in different areas can be recognized by their chemical or physical composition. However, this is not so. The factor which is by all odds the most important in assigning an age to a given stratum is its biological content — that is, the *fossils* it contains.

> Thus it appears that the only presently available rational geochronological indices are biostratigraphically based — i.e., *biochronologic*.[15]

This means plainly that *only* the fossils can be relied upon as a criterion for determining the time in earth history when a particular formation was deposited. Other data — vertical position, physico-chemical characteristics, and other factors — are essentially insignificant.

> Physico-geometrical data (apart from radiometric) can do no more than provide a crude local relative chronology or circumstantial evidence in support of a biochronologic framework.[16]

Now the only way in which the fossil contents of a rock could

---

[15]T. G. Miller: "Time in Stratigraphy," *Paleontology*, Volume 8, February 1965, p. 119. Emphasis his. Miller is at Keele University in Staffordshire.

[16]*Ibid.*, p. 128.

possibly indicate how old the rock might be is if the animals found as fossils were living only at that specific time in earth history. This means that there have been different kinds of life at different periods in history, and that therefore the living forms provide an unambiguous index to the chronology.

But how do we know which forms were living when? There must be some systematic way of viewing and classifying the changes of life forms with the passage of geologic time. The key, of course, is evolution! If we are to explain everything in terms of uniform laws and uniform processes, this must include the development of the biological world as well as the physical world. All kinds of animals must therefore have gradually developed from earlier and simpler forms. There must have been a slow increase of organization and complexity of living forms during geologic history. And this is the clue we need! Simple fossils mean a formation is ancient; complex fossils are recent.

The fossil record thus is of absolutely paramount importance in geologic dating. The fossil forms are classified according to the underlying evolutionary assumptions, and then they in turn become "index fossils" for future dating purposes.

> In each sedimentary stratum certain fossils seem to be characteristically abundant: these fossils are known as *index fossils*. If in a strange formation an index fossil is found, it is easy to date that particular layer of rock and to correlate it with other exposures in distant regions containing the same species.[17]

The evolutionary significance of this methodology is clearly indicated by the following:

> Once it was understood that each fossil represents a biologic entity, instead of a special divinely created life form, it became quite obvious that the plants and animals of each stratigraphic division had simply evolved from those of the preceding epoch through gradual adaptation. They were, in turn, ancestral to those that followed.[18]

This technique might have merit if it were actually known, from historical records or from divine revelation or from some other source, that in fact all living forms had actually evolved from prior forms. But the actual evidence for evolution on such a scale as this is, as implied by the above quotation, limited to the fossil record itself. In a presidential address before the Geological Society of America, Dr. Hollis Hedberg also stressed the evolutionary significance of the fossil record, as follows:

> That our present-day knowledge of the sequence of strata in the

---

[17]J. E. Ransom: *Fossils in America* (New York, Harper & Row, 1964), p. 43.
[18]*Ibid.*

earth's crust is in major part due to the evidence supplied by fossils is a truism. Merely in their role as distinctive rock constituents, fossils have furnished one of the best and most widely used means of tracing beds and correlating them. However, going far beyond this fossils have furnished, through their record of the evolution of life on this planet, an amazingly effective key to the relative positioning of strata in widely separated regions and from continent to continent.[19]

Thus, the primary means of dating rock formations relative to each other, in the Geologic Column, is the evolutionary sequence of life on the earth through geologic time, and the preservation of distinctive life forms as fossils deposited in the rocks laid down during each successive period. But, then, in turn, the history of evolution on the earth has been built up on the basis of the record revealed in the rocks representing the successive geologic ages. In fact, the only genuine historical evidence for the truth of evolution is found in this fossil record. As Dunbar says:

> Although the comparative study of living plants and animals may give very convincing circumstantial evidence, fossils provide the only historical, documentary evidence that life has evolved from simpler to more and more complex forms.[20]

The evidence for evolution afforded by living plants and animals is, indeed, hardly convincing at all. The almost universally accepted biologic mechanism for producing evolutionary change is supposed to be genetic mutation (a sudden, random change in the biochemical structure of the germ cell) preserved, if favorable, by natural selection.

This is confirmed by the very prominent Edinburgh geneticist, C. H. Waddington:

> It remains true to say that we know of no way other than random mutation by which new hereditary variation comes into being, nor any process other than natural selection by which the hereditary constitution of a population changes from one generation to the next.[21]

Since our focus of attention in this paper is geology, we do not wish to digress into a discussion of genetic theory at this point, except to call attention to the fact that *present* processes of biologic change are associated almost exclusively with mutations, as far as permanent, hereditary, truly novel changes are concerned. Presumably if evolution is actually a fact of nature, it is to be

---

[19]H. D. Hedberg: "The Stratigraphic Panorama," *Geological Society of America Bulletin*, Volume 72, April 1961, pp. 499-518.

[20]C. O. Dunbar, *op cit.*, p. 47.

[21]C. H. Waddington: *The Nature of Life* (New York, Atheneum, 1961), p. 98.

explained in terms of mutation and natural selection. This, in fact, is undoubtedly the consensus of the thinking of most leading evolutionists today, not only those working in the field of genetics, but also those in the field of paleontology.

Furthermore, it is admitted by all geneticists that the great majority — in fact, almost *all* — mutations are basically harmful. This is only to be expected, since they represent random changes in very highly-ordered systems:

> Mutations occur at random, not because it would be convenient to have one. Any chance alteration in the composition and properties of a highly complex operating system is not likely to improve its manner of operation and most mutations are disadvantageous for this reason. There is a delicate balance between an organism and its environment which a mutation can easily upset. One could as well expect that altering the position of the foot brake or the gas pedal at random would improve the operation of an automobile.[22]

As a matter of fact, mutations provide a very fine illustration of the second law of thermodynamics — the universal tendency toward disorder and decay. In any case, truly beneficial mutations are obviously such very rare events, if they occur at all, that it is quite impossible to see real evolution occurring among present plants and animals. There is, of course, a great deal of variation, within basic kinds of creatures — in fact, no two individuals are exactly alike — but there are also quite clear-cut gaps between such basic kinds of creatures.

Since evolution cannot be demonstrated as occurring in the present, and since, indeed, such evidence as does exist of biologic change in the present seems to be evidence of decay and death, rather than growth and increasing organization, it is obvious that, in the last analysis, the only real evidence for evolution in the broad sense is that contained in the fossil record.

But the fossil record is based on the geologic ages, and the geologic ages have been built up as an interpretive framework for earth history on the very basis of the assumption of evolution! This is obviously circular reasoning, but that in itself does not condemn it since, in the final analysis, all philosophies are based on circular reasoning. One always brings certain innate presuppositions with him when he tries to philosophize on origins and meanings, and these necessarily determine his conclusions. It is only when such circular reasoning is called *science* that it really becomes scientism. As a religious faith, it may be a live option, but not as science!

---

[22]Frederick S. Hulse: *The Human Species* (New York, Random House, 1963), p. 53.

Basic Inconsistencies in Evolutionary Uniformitarianism

The fallacious application of uniformitarian reasoning to geological process rates thus has led to the system of the evolutionary geologic ages. This in turn forms the evidential basis of the theory of evolution, which presumably accounts for the origin and development of all things, including life and including man. All of this, as we have just seen, involves a powerful system of circular reasoning, somewhat disguised but nonetheless real.

But there is another, perhaps even more significant, fallacy in this system, which will now be discussed. True uniformitarianism involves the constancy and reliability of natural laws. These laws are formulated to describe the processes of nature, and by their very nature, as concepts developed by scientific measurements and methods, these processes are known only in their *present* form. As noted earlier, these laws deal basically with the concepts of energy and entropy, and are ultimately structured around the two laws of thermodynamics.

The most basic and universal of all scientific laws is that of conservation. There are, of course, a number of different conservation laws (energy, mass, momentum, electric charge, etc.,) but the most important is that of energy (including mass, as a form of energy).

> The physicist's confidence in the conservation principles rests on long and thoroughgoing experience. The conservation of energy, of momentum and of electric charge have been found to hold, within the limits of accuracy of measurement, in every case that has been studied. An elaborate structure of physical theory has been built on these fundamental concepts, and its predictions have been confirmed without fail.[23]

Thus, the basic structure of the universe, in so far as *science* knows it, is conservative. That is, nothing is now being created or destroyed. The present processes of nature, *including all geologic processes and all biologic processes,* are not creative in nature.

Consequently, it is fundamentally impossible for science to learn anything about origins. Science deals with present processes, and present processes are conservative, not creative. Thus, historical geology, professing to discover the history of the origin and evolution of the earth and its inhabitants through a scientific study and extrapolation of present processes, is a self-contradiction.

And the situation becomes even more contradictory when the second law of thermodynamics is considered. Not only is the

---

[23]Gerald Feinberg and Maurice Goldhaber: "The Conservative Laws of Physics," *Scientific American,* Volume 209, October, 1963, p. 36.

universe basically conservative in quantity, but it is also basically degradational in quality.

> Man has long been aware that his world has a tendency to fall apart. Tools wear out, fishing nets need repair, roofs leak, iron rusts, wood decays, loved ones sicken and die, relatives quarrel, and nations make war . . . We instinctively resent the decay of orderly systems such as the living organism and work to restore such systems to their former or even higher levels of organization.[24]

Thus, all systems, no matter how large or how small, living or non-living, tend to become disordered and disorganized, to decay and die. Application of an excess of ordering energy from outside the system is continually needed to offset this decadent tendency, and even more is needed if, for a while, the system is to manifest a period of growth and integration.

There could hardly be imagined a philosophy more in fundamental contradiction with this actual and unquestioned law of nature than the philosophy of evolution. According to evolution, there is an innate principle of development and progress in the universe, leading always to higher and higher levels of complexity and integration.

> Most enlightened persons now accept as a fact that everything in the cosmos — from heavenly bodies to human beings — has developed and continues to develop through evolutionary processes. The great religions of the West have come to accept a historical view of Creation. Evolutionary concepts are applied also to social institutions and to the arts. Indeed, most political parties, as well as schools of theology, sociology, history, or arts, teach these concepts and make them the basis of their doctrines. Thus, theoretical biology now pervades all of Western culture indirectly through the concept of progressive historical change.[25]

We would agree completely that modern science reveals a concept of universal change — but this change is one of decay and dissipation. The supposed universal process of evolution, on the other hand, postulates a universal law of progress and increased organization. Thus, the theory of evolution and the second law of thermodynamics squarely confront and contradict each other. Each is precisely the converse of the other. One is a universal law of change upward, the other a universal law of change downward! It should be plain and obvious that only one of these principles can possibly be valid.

Herein is another, and climactic, contradiction in evolutionary

---

[24]Van Rensselaer Potter: "Society and Science," *Science,* Volume 146, November 20, 1964, p. 1018.

[25]Rene Dubos: "Humanistic Biology," *American Scientist,* Volume 53, March 1965, p. 6.

historical geology. Historical geology purports to tell us of the evolutionary development of life on the earth, and to do so in terms of *present* processes. But present processes are processes of decay, and therefore contradict the very concept of evolution.

If historical geology would be truly scientific, as it clams to be, then it must recognize that it must be organized within the framework of *true* uniformitarianism, which is uniformity of natural law. It must realize that the story of earth history which it seeks to decipher has been one enacted within the framework of laws of conservation and decay, not of creation and development.

Therefore, to assume that the origin and history of the earth can be interpreted within the framework of an assumed uniformity of process rates and an assumed innate principle of evolutionary development is to reject the very basic laws of science which it professes to follow. But this would still be a permissible point of view to take, since not even uniformity of natural law can be *proved* in the prehistoric period. It is legitimate to assume, if one wishes to do so, that the two laws of thermodynamics were not in operation during the geological ages, and therefore that evolution and progress were possible on a worldwide scale. The paleontologic data can then be interpreted to fit into that framework if one wishes so to do. All the contradictions and anomalies which abound in such a system can all be explained away by piling hypothesis upon hypothesis (e.g., explaining great areas where "young" fossils are buried beneath "old" fossils by means of the theory of the overthrust fault). Since all of this can never be subjected to laboratory verification, and is thus out of reach of the "scientific method," this framework of evolutionary uniformitarianism cannot be disproved scientifically.

But to say that a system erected upon such assumptions, which contradict the basic laws of science, is itself "scientific" is entirely unwarranted. And when the theory of evolution, based as it is upon this system, and the paleontologic data interpreted in accordance with it, is then made the foundation for all modern studies in theology, sociology, history, politics, and the arts — indeed into an all-embracing world-view — and when all of this monstrous system is taught and indoctrinated as *scientific fact* almost everywhere, as it is today — the charge of *scientism* is a gross understatement of the true situation!

Implications of Evolution

The system of evolutionary uniformitarianism is, therefore, not a science but a system. It is a form of religion, a faith in innate progress, in materialistic development, in pantheistic humanism. It is the essence of modern man-centered culture. The evolutionary philosophy, as noted by Rene Dubos[26] has profoundly affected every field of human thought and activity. Man has been led to see himself as organically linked to all other forms of life:

> Comparative biology has revealed, furthermore, that man is linked to all living organisms through a common line of descent, and shares with them many characteristics of physicochemical constitution and of biological organization; the philosophical concept of the "great chain of being" can thus be restated now in the form of a scientific generalization.[27]

Not only so, but since all things can be explained in terms of this supposed universal process of evolution, effectuated by the cybernetic processes of mutation and natural selection, there is no need any longer to postulate a divine Creator originating or guiding the development of the universe. God becomes an unnecessary hypothesis. Man, as the highest stage of the evolutionary process, now having come to understand and even to guide it, is himself the creator.

> What is almost certain, however, is that the various components of human culture are now required not only for the survival of man, but also for his existential realization. Man created himself even as he created his culture and thereby he became dependent upon it.[28]

In the last analysis, then, evolution is a religion that permits man to divest himself of concern for or responsibility to a divine Creator. It is not a science in any proper sense of the word at all. And the same must therefore be true for the system of evolutionary historical geology which both supports it and is supported by it.

We hasten to say again that this is no criticism of the sciences of geology or biology, or of the scientists who practice them. The genuine sciences of geology and biology, dealing as they do with the *present* processes of the earth and of life are of highest merit and importance. It is believed that the great majority of geologists and biologists, who may nominally subscribe to the concept of evolution and the geological ages, have never fully considered its implications and that many of them would refute it if they did, professionally costly though such a stand might become.

It is not surprising, in view of the foregoing, that the system of evolution has been appropriated as the pseudo-scientific basis of every political or philosophical system of the past hundred years which has been opposed to Christianity, or even to theism in

[26]Rene Dubos, *supra.*
[27]*Ibid.,* p. x.
[28]*Ibid.,* p. 8.

general. In particular has this been true of the various forms of modern "liberalism," including socialism, fascism and communism.

The influence of Darwinism upon Marxism has been especially significant:

> Orthodox Marxian socialists in the early years of the twentieth century felt quite at home in Darwinian surroundings. Karl Marx himself, with his belief in universal "dialectical" principles, had been as much a monist as Comte or Spencer. Reading *The Origin of Species* in 1860, he reported to Friedrich Engels, and later declared to Ferdinand LaSalle, that "Darwin's book is very important, and serves me as a basis in natural science for the class struggle in history." On the shelves of the socialist bookstores in Germany the works of Darwin and Marx stood side by side.[29]

The views of a prominent contemporary historian, Dean of the Graduate Faculties at Columbia University, are significant:

> It is a commonplace that Marx felt his own work to be the exact parallel of Darwin's. He even wished to dedicate a portion of *Das Kapital* to the author of *The Origin of Species*.[30]

Some of the reasons for this feeling of debt on the part of Marx are discussed as follows:

> It is that, like Darwin, Marx thought he had discovered the law of development. He saw history in stages, as the Darwinists saw geological strata and successive forms of life. . . . But there are even finer points of comparison. In keeping with the feelings of the age, both Marx and Darwin made struggle the means of development. Again, the measure of value in Darwin is survival with reproduction — an absolute fact occurring in time and which wholly disregards the moral or esthetic quality of the product. In Marx the measure of value is expended labor — an absolute fact occurring in time, which also disregards the utility of the product.[31]

To similar effect is the definitive historical evaluation by Dr. Gertrude Himmelfarb:

> There was truth in Engels' eulogy on Marx: "Just as Darwin discovered the law of evolution in organic nature, so Marx discovered the law of evolution in human history." What they both celebrated was the internal rhythm and course of life, the one the life of nature, the other of society, that proceeded by fixed laws, undistracted by the will of God or men. There were no catastrophes in history as there were none in nature. There were no inexplicable acts, no violations

---

[29]Richard Hofstadter: *Social Darwinism in American Thought* (New York, George Braziller, Inc., 1959), p. 115.

[30]Jacques Barzun: *Darwin, Marx, Wagner* (2nd. Ed., New York, Doubleday, 1958), p. 8.

[31]*Ibid.*, p. 170.

of the natural order. God was as powerless as individual men to interfere with the internal, self-adjusting dialectic of change and development.[32]

It is possible to trace similar direct connections between evolutionism and fascism, as well as other philosophical and political symptoms of the basic antipathy to God which seems to afflict a substantial segment of mankind. Perhaps of more immediate concern is the fact that evolutionism is of predominant influence in the system of John Dewey, the chief architect of modern educational theory in this country.

But this is another story, and would carry us too far afield from the content of this study. Our point is simply that the presently accepted system of evolutionary uniformitarianism in the so-called historical geology has projected its influence deeply into almost every sphere of human thought and that, in general, this influence has been highly inimical to the cause of Biblical Christianity. It is thus of immense concern to people in every walk of life and cannot be left simply to the self-assumed authority of those who claim jurisdiction over this field.

The Biblical Framework

The study of origins, destinies and meanings is thus properly to be considered as outside the domain of science. Science deals with present processes, and present processes are conservative and degradational, not creative and organizational. Understanding of the creation and organization of the universe into its present form is therefore to be obtained from other sources than science. Religion necessarily enters the picture.

As noted, evolution is one such possible religious explanation for the universe. But such, it explicitly contradicts what we know about the present world, which operates in accordance with the first and second laws of thermodynamics.

It is far more reasonable to recognize that neither the data nor the processes nor the methods of modern science can lead to an understanding of origins. And certainly, then, the unaided speculations of human reasonings cannot do it. Therefore, divine revelation is required if we are ever really to know anything about the Creation — its date, its duration, its methods, its order, or anything else about it.

It is eminently reasonable, therefore, to reorganize the data which we have obtained in our studies of the universe and its

[32]G. Himmelfarb: *Darwin and the Darwinian Revolution* (London, Chatto & Windus, 1959), p. 348.

inhabitants in terms of the Biblical framework given us by revelation. The Biblical framework does give a perfectly satisfying system for harmonizing all the data of biology, geology, and paleontology, as well as other sciences.

The Bible record describes a special Creation of all things, fully functioning from the very beginning, complete and finished by creative and formative processes no longer in operation, now being sustained by God in accordance with the conservation principle enunciated in the first law of thermodynamics. It also describes a Fall of man, and God's Curse pronounced on the earth, introducing a universal law of decay and disorder, in accordance with the second law of thermodynamics, which for the first time brought disharmony and death into the world. It then describes a great world-destroying Flood in the days of Noah, which completely changed the first cosmos and its structure and processes. It indicates, then, that since the Flood there has been an essential uniformity of both laws and processes, which can thus now be studied and elucidated by the scientific method.

It will be found, if enough study is devoted to it, that all the real data of the fossil record, of biological mechanisms, of geologic processes, and of all natural phenomena, can be oriented and understood within this framework. Such a system will be fully consistent with both the basic laws of science and history and the data of divine revelation.

XVI

CHRIST IN CREATION

"For the invisible things of him from the creation of the world are clearly seen, being understood by the things that are made, even his eternal power and Godhead, so that they are without excuse" *(Romans 1:20).*

According to this remarkable verse of Scripture, there is a clear witness to the God of Creation to be seen in the created universe. Thus there is no difference; every man who has ever lived has been confronted with this testimony of Creation to the nature of the God who made it. Whether or not he ever opens the pages of Holy Scripture, or whether he believes what he reads therein, he cannot escape confrontation with the Christ of Creation! He is without excuse.

But how can this be? "No man hath seen God at any time" (John 1:18). How is it possible that the "invisible things" of God can be made visible, so that they are "clearly seen"?

These "invisible things" are summed up in two great concepts, those of His "eternal power" and His "Godhead." Or, one might say, His work and His person. The fact that He is a God of infinite and eternal omnipotence, one of "eternal power," is revealed plainly, according to this verse, in the created universe. Furthermore, His very nature, His "Godhead," is also revealed in Creation. And this means that *Christ* is revealed in Creation, for the very essence of the Godhead is found in Jesus Christ. *"For in him dwelleth all the fulness of the Godhead bodily"* (Colossians 2:9).

The very Godhead which is clearly revealed in nature by the "things that are made" (Greek *poiema*, the word from which we transliterate our English word "poem," and thus signifying His "poetic handiwork," a word only used elsewhere in Scripture in Ephesians 2:10, where it is said that we who are redeemed by His grace are similarly His "workmanship") is thus summed up in all its fulness in the Lord Jesus Christ. There can therefore be no question that Christ has been revealed in the Creation. He is Himself the Creator (John 1:3; Colossians 1:16). He now sustains and upholds the Creation by the word of His power (Hebrews 1:3; Colossians 1:17), and He is the light that lighteth *every* man that cometh into the world (John 1:9).

Now it should go without saying that no man could recognize and receive Christ through this witness of Creation unless the Holy Spirit so draws him that, through a heart made open and willing,

170

he is enabled to see and believe. For if such a preparation of heart by the Spirit is necessary before a man will receive the Lord, even when revealed through the far brighter light of the Scriptures, far more essential must it be if he is to see and believe the much fainter light diffused throughout the Creation. Nevertheless, the light is surely there, for those who really desire to see and know their God! So when a man, of whatever time or culture, glorifies Him not as God, neither is thankful, but becomes vain in his reasonings, he is without excuse. When he changes the glory of the uncorruptible God into an image like that of corruptible man (whether that image be the wooden idol of the savage, or the humanistic, pantheistic, evolutionary philosophy of the intellectual), he is thereby changing the revealed Truth of God into a lie and serving the Creation more than the Creator, and God must give him up (Romans 1:21-25).

His Eternal Power

The reservoirs of power in the created universe are so vast as to be completely incomprehensible in their fulness. The earth's energy, for all its physical and biological processes, comes from the sun. But only an infinitesimal fraction of the sun's power is thus utilized by the earth. And there are uncountable billions of suns scattered throughout the universe. The more intensively and thoroughly man probes the universe — whether the sub-microscopic universe of the atomic nucleus, or the tremendous metagalactic universe of astronomy — the more amazingly intricate and grand are God's reservoirs of power revealed to be.

In these chapters we have frequently referred to the two great principles of thermodynamics, which describe the basic ways in which physical power in the universe is manifested. These two all-embracing laws of science affirm that none of this power is now coming into existence, even though 'its form is continually changing and is, in fact, continually being degraded into less useful and available forms. These principles of conservation and decay are common to everyday experience and are likewise substantiated by the most precise scientific measurements.

The continual degradation of power (or, better, energy) in the universe is inseparably associated with the progress of time. That is, as time goes on, the energy of the universe becomes progressively less available for maintenance of its processes. The universe is gradually becoming more and more disordered as its entropy inexorably increases. So inextricably is time now associated with the law of entropy, that Sir Arthur Eddington many years ago gave the second law of thermodynamics the graphic name of "Time's Arrow."

Thus the processes of the universe, in so far as science is able to measure and understand them, are inextricably intertwined with time. And since the available power for continuance of these processes, as tremendously great as it is, is now running down, it is obvious that the source — the beginning — of this power is *outside* of time. That is, it is associated not with time, but with *eternity*. Its beginning was outside of time, and its possible renewal must likewise be outside of time. It is therefore *eternal* power. And all these "things that are made" therefore continually give witness to His "eternal power."

The Godhead

Not only does the Creation testify concerning God's eternal power, but our text also indicates that it speaks plainly of "His Godhead." This term has been always associated by theologians with the Trinity. The Godhead is said to be the revelation of God as Father, Son, and Holy Spirit, one God in three persons.

The English word "Godhead" occurs in three places in the Bible, in the King James version, in Romans 1:20, Colossians 2:9 and Acts 17:29, as a translation of three slightly different but related Greek words, *theiotes, theotes,* and *theion,* respectively. Although the connotations of the three may be very slightly different the essential meaning in all three cases is that of "Godhood — the fullest essence of that which makes God what He is." It might be translated by "divinity" or "deity," provided it is understood that the term in every case is to be uniquely applied only to the one true God of Creation.

The passage in Acts makes it emphatically clear that no representation made by man — whether physical or mental — can possibly depict the Godhead. Since man was created in the image of God, man is entirely unable to make an image or model which will depict God. God, as Creator, is infinitely above that which He created, and the creature can only know and understand the nature of God in so far as God may will to reveal Himself.

Nevertheless, Romans 1:20 assures us that the "Godhead" may be "clearly seen" and may be "understood by the things that are made." Not by the things which man has made, but by the things which God has made.

The essence of the "Godhood" of God may be comprehended more fully through the final passage where the word occurs. In Colossians 2:9, the Holy Spirit has recorded through the Apostle Paul the amazing fact that in Jesus Christ "*dwelleth all the fulness of the Godhead bodily."* Though no man has seen God at any time, the only-begotten Son hath declared Him. Jesus Christ is the eternal Word made flesh. He that hath seen the Son hath seen the Father. All that God is has been manifested bodily in Jesus Christ. This is the Great God, our Saviour, Jesus Christ!

Whatever, therefore, may be included under the term "Godhead," it surely includes above all else the revelation of God in the Son. Both the essence and the attributes of God are incorporated in the Godhead, and these are manifest to our understanding in the Person of the Son. Surely also, the Godhead conveys the omnipresence, the omnipotence, the love, the truth, the grace — as well as all other aspects and attributes — of God in His fulness. Therefore, though the term may not in itself precisely mean the Trinity, yet it is clear that the older theologians were on the mark when they thought of it in this way. The Biblical revelation of God and His nature has been just this. God is Father, Son and Holy Spirit, one God in three persons. The Father is the eternal Source of all being; the Son is the Eternal Word by which God makes Himself known; the Spirit is the eternal Presence of God, proceeding everlastingly from the Father through the Son into all Creation. Both the Father and the Spirit, being omnipresent, are invisible — yet continually manifest bodily in the Son. God is revealed in time and space, temporally and corporally, in Jesus Christ. It is not accidental that the Scripture says, not that in Jesus Christ once "dwelled" the Godhead; rather it says that "in Him *dwelleth* all the fulness of the Godhead bodily." *Eternally,* He manifests all that God is. He is the everlasting "I Am," the "Word" which was in the beginning, and without Whom not anything was made that was made (John 1:1-3).

The Triune God

When, therefore, the Scripture tells us that the things created are so designed as to reveal the Godhead, we must understand this to mean that Jesus Christ Himself is to be seen in the Creation. And not only the Son, but also the Father and the Spirit, must be discernible in the Creation. Both the fact of God and the nature of God are "plainly understood" by the "things that are made."

That God is a great Person should be clearly evident to all whose hearts and minds are open and willing to learn of Him. Each person is supremely aware of *his own* existence as a person, even if he knows nothing else whatever. That there must be a great Person who has made his own personality and to whom he must therefore somehow be responsible is intuitively recognized by every man. And the modern scientist, above all men, should be able to recognize the implications of his own fundamental scientific principle of cause and effect. Only a Person could be the great First Cause of the individual personalities which constitute mankind.

That God is One is evident from the fact that Creation is one. There is one humanity, one universe (not a "multiverse"). Modern science recognizes this in its continual search for universal laws, unifying principles, underlying unities. And yet, in its unity, the universe is nevertheless one of great diversity and variety. One mankind, but many men — one basic reality, but innumerable inter-relationships. And should not these facts lead any man, perhaps quite subconsciously, to think of God also as a Unity in diversity — as a Person who is One and yet who somehow manifests Himself as more than one?

At first, it might indeed seem that this concept would lead one directly into polytheism or pantheism or both. And as a matter of fact the almost universal drift of the early nations into a pantheistic polytheism may well be understood in these very terms. But more fundamentally this drift probably represents a corruption of an original insight into the Triune nature of the Creator. For the universe is ultimately a Tri-universe, bearing in a remarkable way the reflection of the Tri-une nature of its Maker.

For thousands of years, men have recognized that the universe is a Space-Matter-Time universe. The common phenomena of universal experience are always related to just these three — and no other — physical entities. All phenomena, including all forms of matter and all types of physical and biological processes, take place *in* space and *through* time. The modern relativistic union of space and time in a Space-Time continuum, as well as the recognition that matter itself is basically one form of energy, with energy in some form manifest everywhere throughout time and space, merely verifies and crystallizes this fact of universal experience. The perspective of modern science is clearly that of the universe as a Space-Mass-Time continuum, with each of the three entities essentially indistinguishable from, and co-terminous with, the other two.

One universe, manifested in terms of three conceptual forms, each of which is equally universal, obviously is remarkably analogous to the character of the Triune God as revealed in Scripture. One God, yet manifest in three persons — Father, Son, and Holy Spirit — each equally God and ultimately inseparable. Futhermore, the inter-relationships between the three persons of the Godhead are closely similar to the relationships between the three entities of the physical universe. As the Son manifests and embodies the Father, so the phenomena of Matter represent, as it were, intangible Space in a form discernible to the senses. Though

Space is everywhere, it is itself quite invisible and seemingly unreal, were it not that phenomena of all kinds are continually and everywhere taking place in Space and thus manifesting its existence. The phenomena themselves, when observed sufficiently closely, are found to be themselves essentially nothing but space (the atomic structure of matter, for example, whether conceived as particles or waves, consists almost wholly of space). And yet the phenomena (matter and energy) are most definitely real and discernible to the senses and to measurement.

The Holy Spirit proceeds from the Son, again invisible and omnipresent, with the function of interpreting and applying the nature and work of the Son and the Father. Likewise, Time is the universal concept within which the significance of Space and Matter must be interpreted and applied. Time itself only becomes meaningful in terms of the phenomena and material and processes that are everywhere manifest in space. But at the same time, these phenomena are quite inconceivable except in terms of Time and the individual segments of time during which they are manifested.

The physical universe as we know it, therefore, is in its nature wonderfully analogous to the nature of its Creator. The continuum of Space and Matter and Time — each distinct and yet each inseparably interrelated with the other two and occupying the whole of the universe — is remarkably parallel in character to what has been revealed concerning the nature of God — Father, Son and Holy Spirit, each distinct and yet each inseparably identified with the other two, and each equally and eternally God.

But there is more. Each of the three universals of the physical universe is itself a tri-unity, so that the universe may even be described as a trinity of trinities!

Consider Space, Matter, and Time in turn. As far as Space is concerned, the universe is a space-universe of three dimensions, no more and no less. There is no true reality in a line, or in a plane; these are mental concepts which have no real existence. Reality requires Space, and Space is three-dimensional. Furthermore, each dimension of Space occupies the whole of Space, in like fashion as each person of the Godhead is equally and fully God.

From the natural viewpoint of a man considering the created universe, we could say that the three dimensions, or directions, are the north-south, the east-west, and the up-down directions. Or, for brevity, call them respectively length, breadth and height. Each is infinite in extent and each occupies the whole of Space. In imagination, if only one dimension existed (length, say), even though this dimension be infinitely great, it is impossible even to comprehend or visualize what this would be like. "No man hath seen a line at any time." If one tries to draw a line, be it ever so thin, it nevertheless must have *some* width to it in order to be discernible, and then it is no longer a line, but a plane! Thus, the reality of *one* dimension can only be demonstrated by a construct in *two* dimensions. The second dimension must be present in order for the first to be revealed. The reality of "length" can only be demonstrated by the simultaneous presence of "breadth."

When both length and breadth are available for representation of physical truth, then visualization is quite possible. The "two-dimensional" method of representing physical reality is universally used and, in fact, it is far easier to visualize things in two dimensions than in three. Pictures are painted in two dimensions, construction plans (even for three-dimensional buildings) are drawn in two dimensions, letters are written on two-dimensional sheets of paper, books are printed and read on two-dimensional pages, and so for nearly all *representations* of physical reality. The typical engineering student, for example, in learning how to make engineering drawings, typically finds it far easier to visualize in two dimensions than in three. And, though it is easy enough to visualize *one* dimension, he finds it essentially impossible to represent any reality by only one dimension. The two-dimensional representation is necessary and sufficient for the revelation of both the reality of *one* dimension and of *three* dimensions.

Analogously, the reality of both the One God, the eternal Father, and of the omnipresent Spirit of God is demonstrated and represented visibly by the incarnate Word, the Son of God, the Second Person. Nevertheless, the experimental reality of the Godhead requires more than the recognition of the true existence of the Father as revealed in and by the Son. There must also be experienced the real Presence of God, by the Holy Spirit. "If any man have not the Spirit of Christ, he is none of his" (Romans 8:9). "For through Christ we have access by one Spirit unto the Father" (Ephesians 2:18).

So also spatial reality requires the presence of *depth*, as well as length and breadth. Although reality can be convincingly manifested and represented by means of a two-dimensional visualization, the actual existence of that which is so represented requires all three dimensions. Although a plane can be *seen*, it cannot be experienced! The real world is a world of three dimensions, no more and no less. In summary we can say that the existence of the "length" dimension can only be manifested in terms of the "breadth" dimension and experienced in terms of the "depth" dimension. Though all Space is one, yet it can only be visualized in terms of two of its dimensions and only "lived in" in all three of its dimensions. Just so, the Father can only be seen in the Son and known in the Spirit.

The next in order of the three universals of the physical world is Matter. However, since the proper comprehension of Matter involves an understanding of both Space and Time, we shall by-pass it for the moment and pass on to notice the fundamental triune character of Time.

Now it is wonderful to realize that Time consists of future time, present time, and past time. Each is quite distinct in meaning, and yet each is the whole of Time. All time *has been* future and *will be* past. And in the process whereby future time becomes past time, it passes through the present. The future is the unseen and unexperienced Source of all time. It is made visible and manifest, moment by moment, in the present. It then moves into the past, into the realm of *experienced* time. Man's consciousness of Time pertains only to the present, but this does not lessen the reality or the significance of both the past and the future in his experience and understanding. He is enabled to understand the present, and even to some extent the future, in terms of the past. But both his recollections of past time and his anticipations of future time are visualized in terms of his consciousness of present time.

And again all these relationships and functions are closely parallel to those of the persons in the Godhead. The Father is the unseen Source. From Him proceeds the Son, in Whom He is visibly revealed. From the Son in turn proceeds the Holy Spirit, Who interprets and makes meaningful in actual experience the Son and the Father.

The last entity to be considered, though the second in natural order, is Matter. As noted before, Space is embodied and revealed in Matter, and both are understood and applied in terms of Time. Now it is clear that Matter can only be understood and considered in relation to that portion of Space which it occupies and that duration of Time when it functions. Matter in the broadest sense, of course, is synonymous with Energy. Matter and Energy are interconvertible. As commonly understood nowadays, Matter in fact is merely one form of Energy, and thus the latter term is more comprehensive. For our present purposes, therefore, it is more appropriate to use the term Energy to describe the second great entity in this tri-universe. We shall think henceforth, therefore, in terms of a Space-Energy-Time universe. Energy includes light, heat, sound, electricity, radiation, and all other manifestations of energizing phenomena, capable of producing motion and accomplishing work. And of course it also includes what we commonly think of as Matter, with its atomic and molecular structure, and its characteristics of density and inertia.

Every manifestation of Energy in the universe takes place in Space and Time. For any finite phenomenon, the particular manifestation has a particular location and particular duration, a beginning and ending, both spatially and temporally. It is also profoundly significant that every manifestation of energy necessarily involves some form of motion. Light, heat, sound — all have velocities. The atomic structure of Matter is essentially tremendous motion in space. In fact, it may quite accurately be said that the very presence of Energy is necessarily manifest in Motion. If Energy is present, it will beget Motion. It accomplishes work. There are many different forms of Motion that may be produced, and the particular form will determine the particular phenomenon that is experienced — whether light or electricity or hardness or whatever it may be. This may, in fact, be said to be the basic tri-unity of Matter. First, there is Energy, the unseen but powerful Source, begetting and manifesting itself in Motion (evidenced by a velocity, passing through a certain space in a certain time), and finally experienced in terms of the phenomena produced. Each — energy, motion, phenomena — is inseparably related to the other two and each is universally present wherever there is Matter; in fact, each is Matter. Matter invariably is equivalent to Energy and Energy is invariably manifested in Motion and Motion invariably produces Phenomena.

But there is even a more basic way of understanding the tri-unity inherent in Matter, or Energy. Since every phenomenon has a beginning and end, both in Space and in Time, let us call each such occurrence an Event. In this sense a flash of lightning, a fire, a musical sound, or any other phenomenon is an Event which takes place in Space and Time. The duration may be brief or great and the space occupied may be small or large. Even a mountain or a planet or a star may thus be considered an Event, occupying a certain part of Space for a certain length of Time. We can include under this term not only physical phenomena but also biological and mental and spiritual phenomena. An animal, a meditation, a prayer — all are Events, each with a beginning and end, in Space and Time.

But, after all, it is not quite correct to say that any such Event really has a definite beginning, although its specific manifestation does appear to have such. But associated with the Event is its immediate Cause, and the cause of the Cause, and so on back through a chain of causes to the very beginning of the Creation itself. Similarly, the Event seems to have a definite ending, but actually, the Consequences of that Event continue to spread out through Space and Time, causing other Events as long as the universe endures. Each Event, therefore, is inseparably linked to its Cause and its Consequence. The Cause is the unseen Source of the Event, and the Consequence is that which proceeds from it. And here again is the same basic Tri-unity that pervades all nature.

Thus, in a most remarkable way, the universe is a Tri-universe. The universe as a whole is a Space-Matter (or Energy)-Time continuum. Space is length, breadth, and depth. Time is future, present, and past. And Matter, in the broadest sense is cause, event, and consequence (or energy, motion, and phenomenon). Throughout the universe we see this recurring relationship of Source, Manifestation, and Meaning. These relationships are so basic and obvious that we find it difficult even to wonder about them. They seem axiomatic, part of the necessary structure of things, things that are almost too "clearly seen."

Admittedly this does not *prove* that the Creator of this Tri-universe is a Tri-une God. But with all these worldwide reflections of the Tri-une nature of the Godhead "clearly seen, being understood by the things that are made," men should certainly not stumble over the Biblical revelation of a Tri-une God. This *should* be the most natural way, and undoubtedly *was* the originally revealed way, of understanding the nature of "His eternal power and Godhead."

The Hypostatic Union

Even as there is profound scientific truth in the mystery of the tri-une nature of God, so also there is profound scientific truth in the great mystery of the Incarnation. That Jesus Christ was both man and God, each in the full substance (*hypostasis*) of reality — fully human and yet very God of very God — has been the foundation of Christian doctrine since the time of Christ Himself. The perfect and complete union of the divine and human natures in Christ is so fundamental that its denial is the very identification of the doctrine of Anti-Christ (I John 4:2, 3, 15). Many have distorted or denied the truth of the genuinely human nature of Christ, especially in ancient times; many more have questioned the true Deity of the man Jesus, especially in modern times. Both heresies stress the supposed impossibility of two such completely distinctive natures being consubstantially united in one Person.

And yet essentially the same paradox is reflected throughout the Creation in a marvelous way. That is, each of the three basic entities of the physical Creation itself manifests a paradoxical, complementary duality of essentially the same characteristics as that wherein the Son reveals Himself.

The paradox of the Second Person of the Godhead (in Whom dwelleth all the fulness of the Godhead bodily) lies in the apparent contradiction between the concept of an omnipresent, eternal Being confined within the finite bounds of a human body and the temporal duration of a human life. These terms seem contradictory by very definition.

But it is in the very semantics of this apparent contradiction that we find a remarkable analogy in the nature of the physical Creation. That is, Space is both finite and infinite; and Time is both temporal and eternal. These are the very terms we use to describe the paradox of the divine-human nature of Christ. Although Space is essentially infinite in conceptual extent (we cannot conceive of an end of Space, because what could be outside that save more space?), we can only *understand* and measure it in terms of finite distances. And though Time, in so far as we can conceive it (what could be before, or after, Time?) is essentially flowing eternally, we can only measure and understand it in terms of finite, temporal durations.

In like fashion, though God is essentially infinite and eternal, He can only be understood by finite, temporal man in the terms of finitude and temporality with which man is able to reason and react. In these terms has God revealed Himself to man, in the person of the Son of Man, Jesus Christ.

The great central tri-une reality of the physical Creation has been described as consisting of the Events which take place in Space and Time. Such Events occur in great variety, including all the phenomena of matter, of light, heat, sound, radiation, electricity, and even of life itself. Greatly diverse though these and all other phenomena of nature may appear to be, there is a single underlying unity pervading all of them. Each is essentially some form of Motion (and, of course, Motion necessarily takes place in Space through Time), and further, each is basically a manifestation of some form of Energy. Thus Energy is the basic Cause of every particular Event and its associated Motion. The phenomena which proceed from it (heat, sound, materiality, etc.) are the Effects, or Consequences, as discussed in the preceding section.

"Energy" may be defined as the capacity for accomplishing work. Heat, sound, electricity, chemical energy, mechanical energy, and many other forms of energy exist. Matter itself is essentially a form of energy, and can under the proper conditions be converted into other forms of energy. But undoubtedly the most basic form of energy is Light. It is the light, or radiant energy, from the Sun which is the source of all the varied forms of energy which maintain the earth's physical and biological processes. The sun's radiant energy, in turn, is derived from thermonuclear reactions involving the conversion of matter into energy. Matter is related to other forms of energy in terms of the famous equation of Einstein, the conversion factor involving the square of the velocity of light.

The velocity of light is the most remarkable number in all the physical universe. It is evidently constant under all possible conditions, and is the greatest velocity possible in the physical universe, so far as we know. It is thus the Motion to which all other lesser motions in the universe must be referenced.

We come then to this, that the third great reality of the universe, which we have described under the comprehensive term of the Events taking place in Space and Time, can finally be described simply as Energy, and Energy in turn ultimately as Light! Now, more than by any other aspect of the physical Creation, the Creator, Jesus Christ, is shown forth by the very fact of Light. The first Word of the Creator, uttered in the primeval darkness, was: "Let there be light" (Genesis 1:3). He is the "light of the world" (John 8:12), the "true light, which lighteth every man that cometh into the world" (John 1:9).

One of the most profound discoveries of modern science has been that physical Light (and, therefore, also Matter, in its basic atomic structure) has two natures, apparently contradictory and yet perfectly real and harmonious! Under certain conditions, light manifests all the characteristics of a wave motion; in other situations, it seems to behave as a stream of particles.

This dual nature of light (and of the atomic structure of Matter) has been the greatest paradox of modern science. Some physicists still maintain that this is a contradiction and are hoping that further study will eventually be able to determine whether light is really propagated as waves or as particles. But most scientists are convinced that this duality — they call it "complementarity" — of light is real, even though beyond understanding. It has become the basis of the famous "principle of indeterminacy," which says that it is forever impossible, in the very nature of things, to determine completely the behaviour of the sub-atomic particles which constitute the ultimate basis of Matter. The distances are so small, and the velocities so great, that physical measurements, even in imagination, are incapable of precise determination and decision. The powerful tools of mathematical physics known, respectively, as wave mechanics and quantum mechanics, likewise reflect this fundamental "complementarity" of nature, the one being a means of studying wave motions, the other of motions of particles, or "quanta," each having its own regime of application.

Thus, both the wave nature of light and the particle nature of light are accepted as scientifically valid descriptions of the basic nature of light (and therefore of all Matter). Now one, and now the other, is manifest, but both are real. One might even think of this remarkable reality in terms of a "hypostatic union" of the two natures of light. Analogously, He who is the spiritual Light of the world manifests, in perfect union and complementarity, characteristics of *both* the perfect man and the infinite God! In this remarkable way also does the physical universe — the "things that are made" — witness to the Lord Jesus Christ, in "His eternal power and Godhead," since it is He alone in Whom "dwelleth all the fulness of the Godhead bodily."

The Grace of God

The Scriptures, of course, reveal God not only to be a God of "eternal power," but also to be the "God of all grace" (I Peter 5:10). Since Jesus Christ has manifested not only God's power and holiness, but even more His infinite love and grace, and since He is the bodily incarnation of the whole fulness of the Godhead, which in turn is said to have been clearly revealed in the physical Creation, it is reasonable to ask also whether there may be evidence in nature of the Gospel of the grace of God.

And it does seem that there *is* such evidence, even though its significance would certainly require illumination by the Holy Spirit before it could be appropriated by the natural man. As noted before, even the crystal clear light of Holy Scripture, with its ineffable testimony to both the power and the grace of God in Christ, requires illumination and conviction by the Holy Spirit before its message can be comprehended and appropriated by the natural man. If this is so, infinitely more essential is such illumination before the much more diffuse light in nature could be comprehended and appropriated. Nevertheless, *the Light is there,* so that men who reject the Light (since their deeds are evil, according to John 3:19) are "without excuse."

The message of the Apostle Paul to the pagans in Lystra speaks of this witness of God in nature concerning His grace. He said:

> We also are men of like passions with you, and preach unto you that ye should turn from these vanities unto the living God, which made heaven and earth, and the sea, and all things that are therein: Who in times past suffered all nations to walk in their own ways. Nevertheless he left not himself without witness, in that he did good, and gave us rain from heaven, and fruitful seasons, filling our hearts with food and gladness (Acts 14:15-17).

Thus, according to Paul, there is a witness of God in nature, not only to His power in Creation, but also to the fact that He "did good." He is a God of goodness, and this is evident by His continual provision of the rain and the seasons and all that is necessary for the continuance of life on earth.

But this provision of life's necessities must also be understood against the background of God's Curse on the earth. God had provided "food and gladness" in spite of the fact that He had long ago said, to the very first man, that "in *sorrow* shalt thou eat of it, all the days of thy life" (Genesis 3:17). The "whole Creation" is under the "bondage of decay," and is "groaning and travailing together in pain, until now" (Romans 8:21, 22).

Both the witness of a "cursed" earth, which yields thorns and thistles, and from which a living may be extracted only at the cost of sorrow, and sweat and tears, and the witness of an accusing conscience (Romans 2:15), continuously unite in their reminder to man that something is wrong in the world. There is a great gulf between himself and the great God of Creation, whose eternal power and Godhead should be clearly seen in the things that were made. And above all there is the great enemy, Death, which man ever seeks to escape, but which inexorably overtakes him in the end.

And still there is the ever-recurring testimony of Hope which man sees revealed in the Creation. Though the earth is reluctant, and requires labor and tears to yield its increase, nevertheless the fruit does come. God year by year sends the rain from heaven and the corn grows in its mysterious way. The winter comes, and life seems almost to die away as the Curse becomes more and more evident. But then once again God sends His "fruitful seasons" and the earth is renewed.

And, in fact, every day, there is a reminder of death and darkness and sin. "The night cometh, when no man can work." The light, which is so utterly essential to life, vanishes away each evening, and there is a long night of darkness. But that which might be the source of terror and hopelessness and death becomes instead a time of rest and restoration, because man knows that the sun will rise again the next day. And though he may not know its significance, apart from the Biblical revelation, somehow man has always sensed that the rising of the sun was a testimony to God's provision of healing and life.

Thus, every day, in the sunrise, and every year, in the coming of spring, there is a recurring witness to the Hope of victory over sin and the Curse and death. Somewhere, someday, the "Sun of righteousness would arise, with healing in his wings" (Malachi 4:2). There would someday come a time when the world could say: "For, lo, the winter is past, the rain is over and gone; the flowers appear on the earth; the time of the singing of birds is come" (Song of Solomon 2:11, 12).

Thus there is in nature a wonderful testimony to the grace of God. Though the whole Creation is groaning under the bondage of corruption, and death is the common experience of all animate life, yet there is always the hope of life out of death. Further-more, the fact that the earth's orbital revolution and its axial rotation, which are the physical mechanisms responsible for the annual return of spring and the diurnal return of light to the world, are entirely outside of man's ability to produce by himself *should* cause him to offer up continual thanks and praise to the God who in grace provides these gifts. They should be perpetual reminders that man is unable to save himself; he is helpless in a hostile environment apart from the grace of his Creator. The great Creator must also be his Saviour, or he is utterly lost.

But there is another aspect to God's grace, and this is all-im-portant. God is the God of all grace, but He can only exercise His grace and mercy and love in such a way that His holiness and righteousness are maintained in full integrity. He cannot merely wink at sin. Death is not just an accident, but is in-herent in the very nature of a world which is in rebellion against its Maker. Salvation and light and life can only be provided when sin and the Curse and death have been overcome. But man him-self is no more able to overcome sin and make himself righteous than he is able to defeat the night and cause the sun to rise or to conquer death and rise from the dead.

Only life can vanquish death, and only righteousness can con-quer sin, but this is absolutely impossible for man, who is himself bound by sin and death, to do. If it is done, it must be accom-plished for him by someone else. He must have a substitute, one who can completely take *his* place before God, who can suffer in his stead for his sins and who can also attain full victory over sin and death on his behalf. And this is utterly impossible, except for God Himself, to accomplish. God must be Redeemer as well as Creator and Sustainer. Before true and lasting Life can be pro-vided for dying mankind, God Himself must bear the earth's Curse and die for the sins of the world.

Is there a witness to this greatest of all Gospel truths in Creation? Yes, there is, though as with all reflections, it is far less than the reality. The fact that only out of sacrificial death can come for-giveness and life seems to have been recognized since the begin-ning of human history; all tribes and nations have, in some way or another, recognized that reconciliation with God requires substitu-tionary and propitiatory sacrifice. To what extent the universal custom of sacrifice, distorted and corrupt though it may usually have become, reflects a remnant of knowledge of God's primeval revelation of a coming Redeemer, we do not know. But the prac-tice is too universal to have been accidental.

Perhaps it also is partially a reflection of the universal experience that even natural life can come into the world only when one is willing to experience unique suffering and possibly death itself.

Human birth — in fact, even the birth of all animals — only comes
by way of intense travail, and perhaps even at the cost of the death
of the mother.

A most intriguing illustration of this is found in the twenty-sec-
ond Psalm, that marvelous prophetic description of the suffering
and death of Christ on the cross, written a thousand years before
its fulfillment. In the midst of His sufferings, the Lord Jesus cries in
His heart:

> "But I am a worm, and no man; a reproach of men, and despised
> of the people" (Psalm 22:6).

In the parallel prophecy of Isaiah, it was said that "His visage
was so marred (in fact, literally, "Corruption," personified) more
than any man, and his form more than the sons of men" (Isaiah
52:14), so that truly He seemed like "no man." And Isaiah also
said that He was "despised and rejected of men" (Isaiah 53:3).
But in what sense could He have been said actually to be a worm?

In ancient Israel, as in the modern world, there were many
types of worms, of course, and several different kinds are mentioned in the Bible. But the worm referred to in Psalm 22:6 was a
special worm known as the "scarlet worm." It was from this worm
that a valuable secretion was obtained with which to make scarlet
dyes. As a matter of fact, the same word is sometimes translated by "scarlet" or "crimson."

When the female of the scarlet worm species was ready to give
birth to her young, she would attach her body to the trunk of a
tree, fixing herself so firmly and permanently that she could never
leave again. The eggs deposited beneath her body were thus
protected until the larvae were hatched and able to leave and
enter their own life cycle. As the mother died, the crimson fluid
stained her body and the surrounding wood. From the dead bodies
of such female scarlet worms, the commercial scarlet dyes of
antiquity were extracted.

And what a picture this gives of Christ, dying on the Tree,
shedding His precious blood, that He might "bring many sons unto
glory" (Hebrews 2:10)! He died for us, that we might live through
Him!

Similarly, in greater or lesser measure, wherever there is birth
in the animal kingdom, there is also first a period of travail or
even death. One must suffer in order for another to live. When
this universal truth of experience is combined with all the other
great witnesses which God has left in His Creation, we are indeed
not far from seeing in "the things that are made" not only the
Godhead revealed in His infinite power and Tri-une nature, but
even in His eternal sacrificial grace and love.

This is especially true in connection with human birth. In fact, it was by means of a human birth that God Himself had promised from the beginning to come into the world to bring redemption and salvation. In the very midst of the primeval Curse which He was forced to pronounce on the earth because of man's sin, He also gave the gracious promise of the coming Seed of the Woman, who would someday crush the head of Satan and restore man's lost estate. This First Gospel, as it has been called, given in Genesis 3:15, is also the "everlasting Gospel," to which God has witnessed through the ages, in His physical Creation and in His written Word.

Whenever a babe is born, there is "sorrow in thy conception" (Genesis 3:16), because of the reign of sin and death. But, as the Lord Jesus said: "A woman when she is in travail hath sorrow, because her hour is come: but as soon as she is delivered of the child, she remembereth no more the anguish, for joy that a man is born into the world" (John 16:21).

The birth of a babe is a time of joy and thanksgiving everywhere. And everywhere it bears witness to the promised Son, the Seed of the Woman, who one day would come and would "see of the travail of His soul, and be satisfied" (Isaiah 53:11). It also speaks of the glorious fact that, though "the whole creation groaneth and travaileth in pain together until now," it also "shall be delivered," and a new earth shall be born "into the glorious liberty of the children of God" (Romans 8:21, 22).

God indeed has not left Himself without witness! To the eye of faith and hope and love, surely even the "invisible things of Him are clearly seen," and everywhere one looks in the world, with such eyes, he sees an abundance of evidence of Christ, in Creation.